CIRCLES
— of —
SILENCE

CIRCLES
— of —
SILENCE

DON ROBINS

To you, to me,
Stonehenge and Chartres Cathedral,
the Acropolis, Blenheim, the Albert Memorial
are works by the same Old Man
under different names: we know what He did,
what, even, He thought He thought,
but we don't see why.
W. H. Auden, *Thanksgiving for a Habitat*

SOUVENIR PRESS

To Lech, who shared the first day

First published 1985 by Souvenir Press Ltd,
43 Great Russell Street, London WC1B 3PA
and simultaneously in Canada

ISBN 0 285 62685 X

Typeset by CCC, printed and bound in Great Britain
by William Clowes Limited, Beccles and London

CONTENTS

LIST OF ILLUSTRATIONS

ACKNOWLEDGEMENTS

My thanks are due to many people for helping me to write this book. The manuscript was typed by Carol Barbone and Richard and Helena Jaeschke; the line illustrations were prepared by Duncan MacNeil and drawn by Eileen Barnes, and the photographs, where they are not my own, were taken by Richard and Helena Jaeschke and Duncan MacNeil. The photographs of the Dragon Project and certain of the ancient sites came from the collection of Paul Devereux and John Steele. The exact derivations of the photographs are noted in the text.

I am grateful to the Society of Authors, as the literary representative of the Estate of John Masefield, for permission to quote from his *Renard the Fox*, and to Faber and Faber Ltd. for permission to use extracts from *Collected Poems* by W. H. Auden.

I owe a great debt to the forbearance of my family during the long years of archaeology, both in the study and in the field; particularly to my wife, Zofia, who has invariably borne these vicissitudes without complaint. Lastly, the silent empathy of my cats, grouped around the growing manuscript as I wrote, cannot go unmentioned.

PROLOGUE

The Dragon Project, set up in 1977 to examine the possibility that energy anomalies might be associated with stone circles, has gained a certain amount of notice, even notoriety, as its findings have gradually filtered into the media since the first astounding discoveries at Rollright in Oxfordshire. It soon became apparent that the results of the Project would fill a large volume, but the difficulties in getting all the aspects together were formidable; moreover, to do justice to all the work involved and to make the science respectable, the writing would have to be rather technical and very guarded. Such a book is still some years away and the present volume has therefore been written in response to the keen interest of the general public in the initial findings.

In many senses it is an unusual book, written by a practising archaeological scientist who made the first momentous discoveries of anomalies at Rollright and who, in consequence, is perhaps the best qualified to champion the Project in front of a wide audience. I have combined my personal story of what happened with comments on the whole 'earth mysteries' scenario, writing from the viewpoint of a radical but sympathetic physical scientist whose 'trade' is archaeology. The eventual full account of the Project has not been anticipated and the work of other Project members, while recognised in the text, will be fully acknowledged in the complete volume. I keep very much to the personal odyssey, and try to give a flavour of the excitement of discovery, what it feels like to be uncovering unguessed perspectives into the past. I have ventured into areas where orthodox scientists often fear to tread and I have also tried to bring in aspects that may be unfamiliar: the discussion of stone in Chapter 3, for instance, is central to my own research interests; part of the fundamental study of this aspect of trapped electrons has been carried out by my collaborators and myself, and reported widely in the international scientific literature.

Unlike so many books in this genre, mine does not argue a particular case or interpretation. The results of the initial anomaly studies are described and will be comprehensible even to those readers with little or no scientific background, because we are looking comparatively, and they need to understand very little of the basic science. Few interpretations and fewer speculations are made: these will come later.

In writing this book I have drawn upon my own research interests (and their validation in the international literature); on certain aspects of stone circles, where I have discussed current views and opinions, particularly in relation to our strange findings; and also on ideas of ancient science, where the musings of many non-scientists have been pruned somewhat from the vantage point of a practising researcher. In the course of writing, I uncovered many interesting theories relating to stone circles which I was forced reluctantly to put aside, so that the book would retain manageable proportions. These are stories for another day which I hope to return to.

Don Robins
Sudbury, Middlesex
November 1984

1
STONES IN THE
LANDSCAPE

The past at least is secure.
Daniel Webster

History began in Britain when Julius Caesar came in 55 BC. But, as the Roman conquest developed a century later, the invading legions saw a country littered with the remains of past cultures—stone circles, standing stones, barrows, hillforts—many of which were as remote to them in time as the legions are to us, and more obscure still in that the history of those ancient times was a matter of legend and story, not of written record. But over the last two centuries this prehistory has been partly untangled; and a picture has gradually emerged.

THE ENDURING ENIGMA

Prehistory has no personalities: we do not know the names, thoughts or feelings of the Bronze Age chieftain, now in his barrow, or the lost builders of the circles and henges of Britain. Most of our knowledge of those distant ages, of the daily lives of prehistoric people, comes from the ground, patiently exposed by the spade and sieve of the archaeologist. But above ground stands a whole range of monuments of the period that yield their secrets more grudgingly.

In Britain, foremost among these relics of man's remote past is Stonehenge. Much has been written, over many centuries, about this unique and puzzling structure, and it serves as a prehistoric focus at many levels of interest. But how does one describe Stonehenge? Approaching it by the main road heading west from Amesbury, the casual tourist first sees in the distance a rather small and disappointing jumble of stones on a slight rise, and the reaction is often, 'Surely there is more to it than this?'

To those who persevere, Stonehenge displays its marvels: a veritable prehistoric cathedral in rough and pitted stone, constructed in several phases over many centuries, wonderful even in those fragments that have remained after slow decay and collapse. But the more Stonehenge is explored, the more

13

1. The massive complex of Stonehenge on Salisbury Plain has excited antiquarian interest for centuries, and every age seems to mirror its own endeavours and inspirations in the mighty 'hanging stones'.

questions it provokes. Why was it built? Who built it? Why was it abandoned? The questions put to Stonehenge open a door upon the vast and twilit world of prehistory: although the famous lintelled structures are unique among stone circles, the monument is seen as the final flowering of an astonishing period of prehistory when hundreds of circles and other structures, such as passage graves, were built with the huge stones that have given us our name for the structures themselves—megalithic—and for the vanished society of which these massive stone edifices are the most enduring and enigmatic reminders.

Even today some nine hundred circles survive in Britain, and the associated single standing stones (or menhirs) and stone tombs are legion. Stone circles are found in many countries, some elaborate, others simple, and we may feel sure that this surviving number only represents a fraction of those originally erected. The sheer fame of the 'hanging stones'—as the Saxons christened the circle of Stonehenge for the appearance of its lintels— obscures these facts and has also eclipsed the magnitude of its neighbouring

14

highlands

•• stone circles

Fig 1. Stone Circles in Britain. The distribution of surviving circles seems mostly concentrated in the highland zones. Stonehenge, Avebury and Rollright form a distinct, geographical group in the southern lowlands, although they differ considerably in their construction.

15

circle, Avebury. The scale of this structure, scarcely twenty miles from Stonehenge, with its steep embankments, avenues and multiple circles, dwarfs Stonehenge, and its presence prompts another range of questions: did the same people build both structures? Were they in use at the same time? Was there rivalry, competition, even war, between the folk of the two circles? How does one even begin to find the answer to these questions?

Over the last two centuries increasingly careful excavation, with the more recent addition of a developing range of scientific techniques, has built up a painstaking picture of the times when the circles were built and of the way of life of the people who lived then. The broad sweep of this archaeological canvas must form the backdrop for any theory or idea put forward to explain the building and purpose of the circles, whatever one feels about the value of material evidence in trying to understand the hopes, fears and beliefs of a long vanished people. Many explanations proposed, however, tend to disregard this evidence, instead reflecting the value- and belief-systems of their own times, in much the same way as historical feature films faithfully mirror current political beliefs rather than historical facts. The early antiquaries saw the circles as religious monuments in keeping with the age of faith, but the growth of science encouraged the interpretation of the circles as scientific instruments. The concepts of the 'new age' have

2. The densely packed stones of Stonehenge are overshadowed by the immensity of Avebury, twenty miles to the north. Although few of the massive sarsens remain standing, the vast size of the embankment and ditches is emphasised by the mediaeval village which straddles the enclosure and the main road which bisects the site.

16

encouraged devotees to see the circles as focuses of natural energy, erected in an ideal 'golden age' by primaeval ecologists, in harmony with their natural environment. Running through any history of ideas about the circles, however, is a persistent thread of magic, of a knowledge once enshrined in the circles and then lost for ever.

The very silence of the circles and their lack of material evidence in the associated soil encourages unbridled speculation, and this silence is often taken for agreement. In this book, however, I shall describe an attempt to look at the circles as they are, without expecting evidence to support a particular idea, and we shall see that, in this way, whole new series of questions are generated.

But let us first take a closer look at the prehistoric background to the circles and at the views, both ancient and modern, sober and wild, put forward to explain their erection.

GRAVEYARD OF ANTIQUITY

Stonehenge does not stand alone. Other people were on Salisbury Plain before it was first raised and others came after it was abandoned; that whole area of southern England has been settled continuously for the last six thousand years at least. A glance at the Ordnance Survey map of the Stonehenge and Avebury areas bears this out convincingly: structures and relics from all periods of British history are scattered, meshed and overlaid in bewildering profusion. The oldest monuments are the long barrows—communal graves of the first farmers of the New Stone Age (neolithic) built some six thousand years ago. The circles and standing stones come between these long graves and the round barrows of the Bronze Age chieftains who lived some fifteen hundred years before Christ. Apart from graves, stone circles and standing stones, vast earthworks scour the valleys and downs and sculpt the hilltops, many dating from the millennium before the Roman invasion, when the country was invaded from the European mainland by the Iron Age Celts.

Much of this prehistoric heritage was doubtless lost in the taming of the land in Roman and Saxon times, when the mattock and plough brought down proud monuments that invaders in previous time could not overthrow. What we now see is but a fraction of what once existed and it is overlaid by Roman, Saxon and mediaeval developments—roads, forts, camps, villages and feudal field systems which in turn are obliterated, wholly or partially, by modern energy and communication networks, industrial and housing developments and, particularly on Salisbury Plain, by the extensive army training grounds.

17

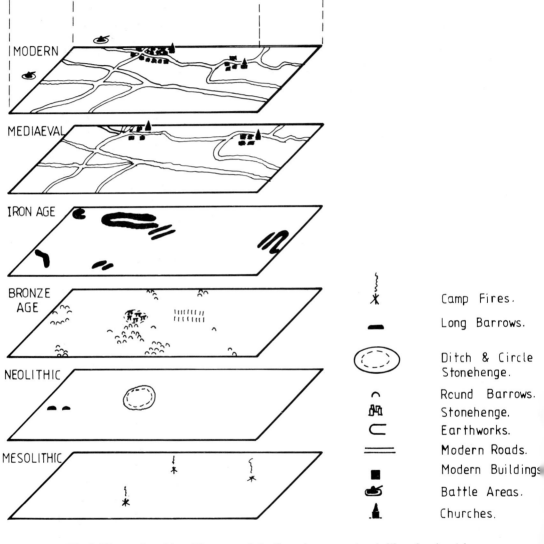

Fig 2. History in a Map. The map of the Stonehenge region is like a book with every page representing a particular period of the past. These pages can be prised apart to give an idea of how human occupation has changed and developed over the centuries.

18

3. Many standing stones, isolated or in groups, stud the British countryside. Some, like the Hoar Stone at Enstone, Oxfordshire, are all that remain of a burial chamber or barrow.

This vast graveyard of antiquity is mirrored in many other parts of the country, but it is in the wilder, mountainous western fringes of Britain, where historical developments have been less dense, that the megaliths have their greatest concentration. Viewed in this light, the vast enterprises at Stonehenge and Avebury and the lesser undertaking at Rollright—which figures so largely in the story of this book—are among the most far-flung examples of the surviving circles and long barrows, built during the millennium around 2000 BC, which are concentrated along the western seaboard of mainland Britain from Cornwall to the Orkneys. A vast development on the east coast of Ireland, around the mouth of the Boyne river, parallels this seaboard concentration, and further south it is continued all along the Atlantic coast of Europe, through France, Portugal and Spain, achieving a spectacular flowering in Brittany with the stone rows of Carnac.

This distribution of the megaliths, their linking to the early agricultural phase in Europe, and their erection over a relatively short time scale, has led some to suggest that they were built by a migrating people who went by sea along the Atlantic coast from a starting point in Southern Spain or North

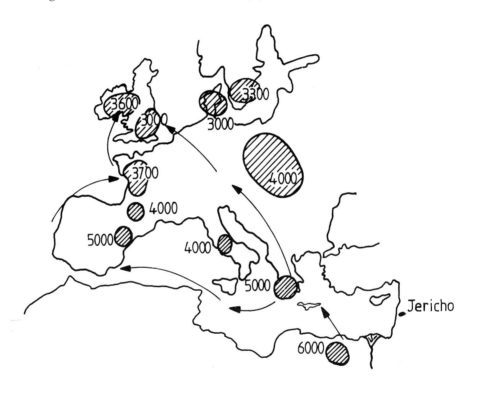

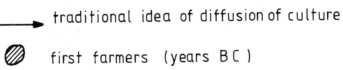

Fig 3. How the First Farmers Came to Britain. The 'diffusionist' view of archaeology that is supported by establishing when the first farmers were active in Europe. The spreading from the Near East to Britain is based upon radiocarbon dates of these sites.

Africa. This idea brings us uncomfortably close to the diffusionists who see all European culture deriving from the early civilisations of the Near East, and it surfaces in megalithic terms in suggestions that Egyptian or Greek architects designed the structures, using the local Stone Age populations as willing or slave labour. The radiocarbon recalibration in the last decade has tended, however, to push the dates for the earliest megalithic structures beyond even the Egyptian horizon and diffusionism is currently out of fashion; if anything, it could even be suggested in reverse!

The building of the megalithic monuments nevertheless required substantial labour, and it is possible that seaborne invaders may have persuaded or forced a local population to co-operate in the vast construction projects. Furthermore, some of these invaders seem to have come through the western 'back door', avoiding the traditional south-eastern approach favoured by all successful, and most unsuccessful, invaders of Britain.

But what does the evidence of the spade tell us about the people of that time—both the megalith builders and those already in the islands? What do we know about everyday life some four thousand years ago and the kind of people who built these huge structures?

4. The whole countryside of Britain is marked with traces from all periods of antiquity, and the earth works on hill tops are often the most obvious. This hillfort, at Burrough Hill near Melton Mowbray in Leicestershire, dates from the Iron Age and its steep ramparts now guard the empty turf of the hill-top enclosure. (Photo: Duncan MacNeil)

21

HOW WE LIVED THEN

The popular clichés of the woad-painted savage and the shambling caveman have no place in the story of megalithic Britain: the people who lived then were the same as us, despite the seeming simplicity of their lives and the grinding routine of the agricultural year that undoubtedly hovered on the subsistence line. Throughout the entire megalithic period we see a gradual increase in technical and social complexity; the rate of change was much slower than in recent times, but it existed in a way that modern stone age societies, which had been essentially static for millennia until the western onslaught in the nineteenth century, have never experienced.

The megalithic period lasted from about 3000 BC to 1500 BC and covered the period, in Britain, of the New Stone Age, the time when farming developed in these islands. The megaliths must be seen in the context of these early farmers and also, towards the end of the megalithic era, of the change from a stone-based technology to the advent of copper, first as a decoration, later as a material for weapons, in the chalcolithic period.

Before the advent of the first farmers, presumably as part of a migration from central or northern Europe, the traces of man in Britain are slight. In one sense this is inevitable, because the long millennia of the ice ages have effectively scoured any evidence from the face of the land except in certain areas of the south. The story of the ice age, with the complex advances and retreats of the great glaciers, is one that concerns us here only in its impact on human settlement. After the last retreat of the ice, about ten thousand years ago, traces of hunting bands are detected: their culture of finely made flint and bone hunting weapons is termed mesolithic and lies between the New Stone Age farmers and the Old Stone Age hunters who occupy the longest phase of mankind's history.

What type of contact the farmers had with the skilled mesolithic hunters can never be discovered, although the general opinion is that some kind of coexistence occurred—aspects of the hunting life were grafted on to the developing practice of farming. The archaeological record of these earliest phases is slight, which makes the monumental aspects even more tantalising, for it was in this earliest period that the greatest enterprises—the first phases of Stonehenge, the construction of Avebury, the huge enclosure of Durrington Walls near Stonehenge, the giant long barrows and the 'British Pyramid' of Silbury Hill—were commenced.

What moved the farmers to undertake these gigantic feats of engineering is the central mystery in any enquiry. The effort involved implies both that food production was sufficient to give people the time and energy to undertake this strenuous and laborious work and that an organisation or motivation (or both) existed to inspire and direct the effort. It is, of course,

5. Prominent on many ridges in Southern Britain are the long barrows, the communal graves of the first farmers of the early neolithic period. Here the tree-crowned mound of the East Kennet long barrow commands a sweeping view of the Wiltshire downs.

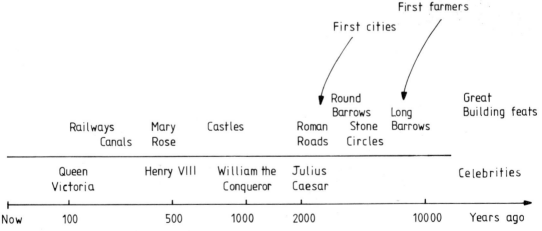

Fig 4. The Past from the Present in Britain. In Britain our history goes back to Julius Caesar, and the vast period between his invasion and the advent of the mesolithic hunting bands after the Ice Age is characterless. The logarithmic scale accentuates the great spans of time and places the stone circles in their technological perspective in Britain's past.

23

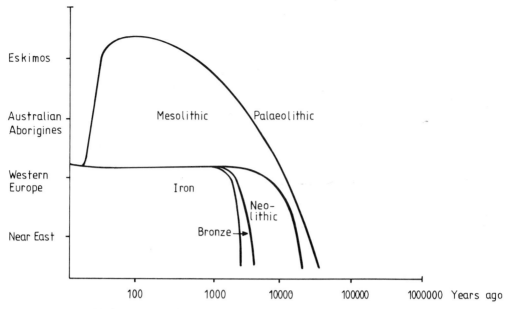

Fig 5. The Movable Feast of Technology. Although the 'Stone Age' ended in Britain some 3,500 years ago, the Australian Aborigines were still in a stone culture when the Europeans came, and the Eskimos retained a highly developed mesolithic culture until recently. The stone circles of western Europe are placed at the junction of the late neolithic and early Bronze Age.

very tempting to read our own ideas, political, ideological or religious, into that remote time, but can we really see the world through the eyes of these first farmers? Could we ever slough off our understanding of the natural world, so painfully acquired since the Renaissance, to go back to the times when, perhaps, every event was controlled by a god or spirit, every action took place under the ever-seeing eyes of a cloud of ghostly ancestors?

Archaeology tells us little about this from the scraps of material remains, and the lessons of anthropology have to be treated with caution, but even to think back to the fatalistic mentality of the Middle Ages, one fostered by the teachings of the Church, helps us appreciate the idea of the unreason that fettered the mind of man. It is the imagination of the novelist, however, that must illuminate this dark stage for us, and all we are left with is a curious paradox: on one hand, simple farming geared to the demands of a northern climate and on the other a seemingly frantic urge to build vast edifices of stone and earth for a purpose we cannot fully understand. To call the stone circles meeting places or ritual centres is almost an admission of defeat, for when the circles themselves are excavated, very little is actually found that tells us about the people who lived then: antler picks used to dig ditches, scraps of pottery, in some cases cremations of children with overtones, at the least, of sacrifice; and very little else. Often the analogy has been made

24

between the effort involved in putting up the circles and the great mediaeval phase of cathedral building: that all this effort was a mirror to faith and an expression of the highest technology of the time. Others, however, have looked in different directions and added another layer to the mystery.

SQUARING THE CIRCLE

Modern attempts to understand the purpose of the circles led to a surprising discovery: many of them seemed to possess an astronomical function, and this conclusion was based upon several strands of evidence.

It seemed that certain stones in the circle were aligned with skyline features and, viewed from the circle, these marked out major astronomical events. The most obvious were the solar standstills—the extreme positions of the sun at the solstices—and the most dramatic example of this is the midsummer sunrise at Stonehenge which is framed by the hanging stones.

But the astronomy did not end there. The moon also has 'standstill' positions, although these are considerably more complex than those of the sun. But the work of Professors Hawkins and Thom demonstrated a whole range of lunar alignments that argued for at least a superficial understanding of the intricate lunar cycle of 18·6 years. More was to come: those sites which did not exhibit convincing solar or lunar alignments could be fitted to star

6. The Wiltshire downland is sprinkled with the round barrows of the Bronze Age aristocracy. This distinctive tree-lined group overlooks the great stone avenue at Avebury.

25

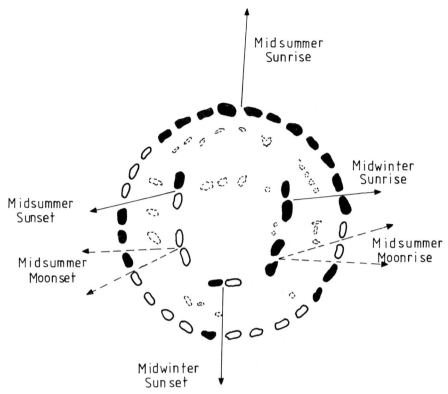

Fig 6. A Circle for All Seasons. The main 'Stonehenge Computer' alignments to the principal solar and lunar standstills. The alignment of lunar standstills poses problems, however, when the stones are now missing (unfilled outlines).

Fig 7. The Alignment Dilemma. Predicting the horizon line-up when stones are missing and there are additional problems with mountainous horizons: which sunrise do we choose?

maps back-calculated three and a half thousand years for the rising of bright and possibly important stars.

There was still more. In surveying many circles over a long period of time, Professor Thom came to the conclusion that, underlying the construction of the circles, was a sophisticated geometrical knowledge that allowed both the creation of 'perfect' circles and elliptical variants, all based upon the unit he termed the 'megalithic yard'.

The development of these two studies—archaeoastronomy and ancient measurement or metrology—continued apace and seemed to point out facets of neolithic life that the potsherds of the archaeologist could not illumine. Here we seemed to have a people skilled in observation and calculation long before the rise of ancient Egypt or Greece. The implication in terms of the archaeological record was clear: the neolithic peasantry supported an elite of astronomer priests who directed their farming activities from the circles— the onset of winter, the coming of spring and the times for harvesting and ploughing. The increased efficiency in farming led to surplus production that kept this priesthood in plenty and allowed them the leisure to develop other pursuits; they refined the circles, perfecting their geometry, setting out both to study the heavens for their own sake—white-robed scientists in search of truth—and also to tame that implacable terror of the ancient world, the eclipse. With a knowledge of eclipse prediction their power grew greater still, and they were wizards, magicians, a closed elite of god-like beings almost worshipped by the awed peasantry who obeyed their every whim and command. Thus, for example, were the stone circles built. This

Fig 8. Megalithic Geometry. Some of the subtle constructions proposed by Professor Thom. It is interesting that these geometries only seem to extend to the shape of the circle and not the spacing or distribution of the actual stones.

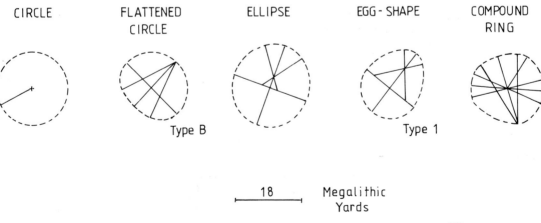

CIRCLE   FLATTENED   ELLIPSE   EGG - SHAPE   COMPOUND
            CIRCLE   RING

Type B   Type 1

18   Megalithic
        Yards

27

picture of an astronomer-priesthood fits neatly into the scenario of megalithic builders spreading up the Atlantic seaboard of Europe from Southern Spain, although the very existence of the vast Stonehenge–Avebury complex could argue equally well for the more traditional invasion route from the south-east.

Without doubt, the notion of an astronomer-elite catches the imagination vividly and the idea has come like manna from heaven to exponents of some of the more outlandish theories of stone circles. Nevertheless, a careful archaeological study by Euan Mackie has added substance to this evolving picture by presenting evidence for some kind of special or elite population at places like Durrington Walls near Stonehenge, and the deserted stone village of Skara Brae. On the other hand, there is always a danger of reading modern answers into the remote past, and however satisfying a discussion of a 'professional priesthood' might be, it implies a social structure that might well exist only in our imagination. Perhaps it is easier to think of unvarying human nature: an exploitation of natural events allowing a cynical group of opportunist strangers to prey upon a simple and trusting native population. This image is in itself an emotive one in terms of recent history, and difficult to transfer with any sense of reality to times when, so far as we know, any concept of national, regional or even group identity might have been absent—or if present, then in a totally alien form.

Coming out from the tempting cloudscape of speculation, we nevertheless see broad agreement on some astronomical function of the circles. The major alignments to the sun are generally undisputed, but fierce controversy rages over many lunar alignments. On jagged mountain ridges the selection of siting features from a circle is often an individual one and the scientist involved in the study may fall unconsciously into Procrustean arguments—every piece of information fitting the picture perfectly to give an overall scenario with no loose ends.

One sees this in the complexity of Hawkins' alignments at Stonehenge and in Thom's selection of skyline points in the Jura mountains. The search for star alignments also falls into this pattern, since the absence of lunar and solar standstill alignments is often taken to mean that there must be *some* other alignment to give purpose to the circle! The classic instance of this is Avebury, where up until now no solar or lunar alignments have been found and Thom has postulated it as a stellar observatory. Some intriguing speculations could arise here on the dense orientation pattern at Stonehenge and its virtual absence at Avebury and also at nearby Rollright. But are the star alignments, which are so evocative and attractive, real or coincidental? Could the stars have been seen against tree cover and through cloud cover? Why were they important?

28

Seductive as the archaeoastronomical idea is, it runs the danger of sweeping away awkward questions in much the same way that any rigid idea-structure does. Why, for example, are so many circles with complex geometrics constructed within a relatively small area of north-west Scotland? Can megalithic 'science for science's sake' really explain this, or does Thom's suggestion that they were used for tidal prediction justify the need for so many? Is the precision demonstrated for some alignments real or imaginary— would it have been so crucial to establish an exact day for planting or harvesting, or would farmers give more weight to the season than the calendar?

7. Castlerigg, Cumbria. This circle, set high in the Lake District amidst a magnificent amphitheatre of mountains, is one of the few megalithic structures shown to have a related geometrical and astronomical function. (Photo: Duncan MacNeil)

Perhaps the most worrying question is where the complex geometrics square with the astronomical alignments. In only one of Thom's enormous number of surveys was there the slightest correspondence—at Castlerigg in Cumbria. In the vast majority of cases the geometry is not required for the alignment, which is invariably based on a single stone, and Thom's demonstration of a very subtle geometry at Avebury uncovered no significant alignments. This is not to deny the reality of the megalithic yard (although it has been said that some of Thom's more involved geometries may owe more to earth movement than megalithic science), neither are the main astronomical features rejected. But there is still a feeling that something in our megalithic picture is lacking.

THE STONES CRY OUT

The various theories put forward to explain the purpose of the circles exert an almost gravitational effect upon the available evidence. Certain types of evidence are pulled towards an attractive theory until the two are tightly meshed, and this interaction applies from the hardest practical archaeology to the softest 'ancient astronaut' theory. But the fact remains: we do not know exactly *when* the stones were erected; we can *infer* this but we have no direct evidence.

Always we are left with the nagging feeling that there is an unexplored aspect of the circles, another factor that will supply the vital perspective and uncover the real purpose of the megalith builders. Unless, of course, there is no such great purpose, only a dull pragmatism!

The idea of astronomer-priests and the efforts of the circle builders have both excited a wide archaeological fringe—the 'off-archaeologists' of Glyn Daniel—and encouraged their wildest speculations and dearest wishes. The building of the circles has been ascribed to such a great variety of causes that it is difficult to sort the wheat from the chaff or even to discover if there is any wheat in this mound of suggestions and ideas.

Is there any way out of this maze? Can the stones be allowed to speak, to show their evidence of the past quite separately from the dry discussions of potsherds, geometry and alignments? Have they been standing there for centuries with all the evidence plainly displayed, requiring only a new approach to unlock their secrets? Out of these questions the idea of 'earth energy' was born and with it the feeling that the circles are the only surviving remains of an ancient science that marked, perhaps even manipulated, some mysterious form of natural energy, the astronomer-priests being the custodians and guardians of this knowledge. And fading into the distance behind this view of the circles is the larger perspective, with the circles aligned into a sacred network, a web of energy whose secrets have been long forgotten, except in the clouded and confused remembrances of folklore.

This was where Dragon Project, and my own involvement, came into the picture. If there were indeed energy associated with the circle or its location, it could be measured as an anomaly against the surrounding landscape. Might this be the road forward in the understanding of the circles—the test for energy anomalies that might explain so many of the puzzling features of these stones in the landscape?

But what energy could be looked for and how could it be interpreted as an anomaly? The answer to this question was to measure first and then decide, and thus to open up a wholly new perspective in the study of the circles—*if* anomalies were detected. Perhaps this would be the route out of the fogs of speculation into the sunlight of science? There was only one way to find out.

2
THE ROAD TO ROLLRIGHT

Seven sarsens of granite grim
As he ran by they looked at him.
John Masefield, *Renard the Fox*

All the efforts to understand the mystery of the circles by orthodox and unorthodox means have either left many unanswered questions or have given answers which remain highly questionable. New light can only be thrown on these enigmas by developing a whole new body of information, and in October 1978 such an attempt began.

DRAGON QUEST

The stones of the circle loomed vaguely through the crawling mist and the trees and grass gleamed with dew in the still, tingling air of dawn. Stepping out of the car in the layby at the Rollright Stones in north Oxfordshire, I felt that I had strayed into the empty set of a horror film rather than embarked on a serious scientific experiment.

It was not yet 8 o'clock on the morning of Saturday, October 21st, 1978. I was at Rollright to carry out the first energy monitoring session of the Dragon Project—an undertaking composed of a diverse group of people interested in exploring the ideas and stories of anomalous energies at prehistoric sites—which took its name from the association of the Dragon symbol with 'earth energy' and its ancient manipulation. Standing in the layby, looking at the stones in the dense white mist, I felt that I had come a long way from reading and speculating about stone circles and their purpose. This expedition was also very different from other scientific tests already reported at such sites (John Taylor's study on the standing stone at Crickhowell had been to test a dowsing response), in that I had no idea what we would find. All I had to work on was a strange first-hand report of anomalous energy at a megalithic site, and the information was so fragmentary and unusual that it gave us the opportunity to monitor physical energy at a circle without really knowing what to expect. Although this was

32

8. The Kingsmen Circle, Rollright, Oxfordshire. The central feature of the megalithic complex is a near-perfect circle of worn and eroded limestone sheltering behind the distinctive belt of trees. The circle has never been excavated but is said to date from the early Bronze Age.

the kind of situation I wanted to be in, to avoid being misled by preconceptions or wish-fulfilment, I couldn't help wondering, in the cold light of dawn which often brings an irritable but penetrating insight, why on earth I was there.

That morning at Rollright, however, was the culmination of many years' interest in stone circles, fostered early on by a childhood absorption in history, but later as a reflection of my disenchantment with the science I practised, as a research chemist in industry and later still in teaching. In this period of disillusionment I had come across books dealing with ley lines, earth energy and similar concepts and had been intrigued with the ideas, and I gradually saw that, somehow and in some way, my science, rusty with disuse, might be brought into play to test some of these ideas and, more importantly, develop new areas.

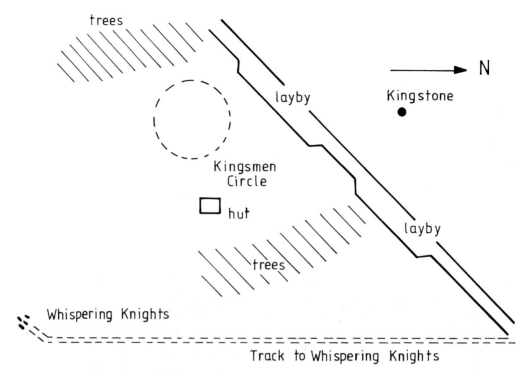

trees

layby

N

Kingstone
●

Kingsmen
Circle

hut

layby

trees

Whispering Knights

Track to Whispering Knights

Fig 9. The 'megalithic laboratory' at Rollright, with dolmen, almost perfect circle and menhir. The Kingstone is actually in Warwickshire: the ancient Oxford-Warwick boundary follows the line of the roadway.

As my interest developed I made contact with others in this sphere and in discussion with Paul Devereux, editor of the magazine *The Ley Hunter*, his long-standing idea of actually searching for these anomalies in a systematic way began to crystallise around the plan of exhaustively testing a stone circle. If, we reasoned, something was found, it might allow all the other anomalous features to fit into place, since stone circles figured large in most unorthodox schemes of archaeology. We saw that we would have to generate a great deal of information within very narrow limits and that the effort would take years, not months. Our tactics, of course, would be dictated primarily by the amount of money available for equipment and the willingness of people to carry out work at stone circles.

The idea gradually evolved, along the lines of so many 'string and sealing wax' efforts that, we fondly felt, were the hallmarks of British improvisation and ingenuity; then, one evening in November 1977, Paul Devereux

34

9. The Kingstone menhir (single standing stone) lies close to the circle but is separated by the ancient lane which forms the county boundary and lies just inside Warwickshire. The weirdly twisted stone stands below the crest of the ridge which figures so powerfully in the Rollright legend.

convened a meeting to discuss the idea of the project, which was at that time unnamed. Some twenty people, from many different backgrounds—scientists, writers, psychics, dowsers, artists—met and tried to hammer out a policy for the work and its funding. The basic framework of the project was settled fairly rapidly: three co-ordinators would oversee the main activities. I would cover the monitoring of physical effects, John Steele, a Californian archaeologist, agreed to organise the human interaction side of the studies and Paul Devereux was to look after the overall logistics of the operation and the co-ordination of effort.

For my part, the question remained: what should we do? Given unlimited resources this question would become easier, but we were severely constrained for the foreseeable future and so had to choose carefully. One question was solved easily, however. That was the choice of a site to study. The owner of the Rollright Stones in north Oxfordshire, Pauline Flick, was sympathetic to our purpose and offered full access for study. Since most of the group were then London-based, Rollright was the most accessible site, but an additional advantage was that the site actually provided a megalithic 'laboratory' in that a single standing stone (or menhir)—the Kingstone—and a collapsed stone burial chamber (or dolmen)—the Whispering Knights—were adjacent, so that an example of each main type of megalithic structure was present for study. Not only that, but Rollright has a rich fund of legend and folklore, to which we shall return in Chapter 5.

But what to do? I had decided that we must break new ground and at the same time accumulate substantial amounts of data for the idea of energy anomalies to be judged fairly, and an intriguing piece of evidence that Paul Devereux had received about a year before our meeting seemed to satisfy most requirements for an anomaly to put to the test.

A zoologist specialising in the study of bat navigation had approached Paul Devereux with a peculiar observation: while investigating bat echo-location with an ultrasonic detector deep in the countryside, he had noted, on returning from a monitoring session, that on passing a megalithic site strong ultrasonic emanations had been recorded. These, he suggested, were sufficiently unusual to merit further investigation. This intriguing anecdote was far outside anything previously reported and allowed the possibility of testing with portable equipment. Another anomaly mentioned for exploration was that recorded by a scientist with Geiger counters at a Welsh stone circle. Very high readings, far in excess of the overall 'background' levels, had been recorded there. Again, this was something hitherto unexploited as a basis for anomaly research, but the phenomenon lent itself to fairly inexpensive portable monitoring. We determined to construct a suitable ultrasonic detector and buy a Geiger counter.

10. The collapsed dolmen (burial chamber) of the Whispering Knights completes the megalithic stage-set of Rollright. The five tumbled stones rest a quarter-mile from the circle and like the Kingstone are encased in unsightly official railings.

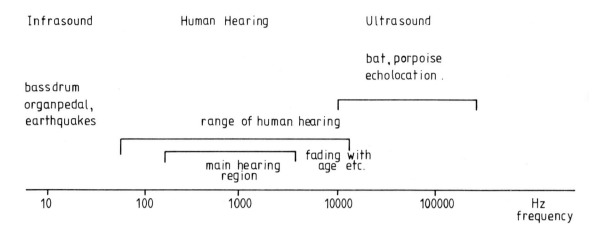

Fig 10. Sound and Ultrasound. We can see that the frequency range of ultrasound extends far above that of human hearing and is widely used for echolocation by animals. An interesting feature of increasing the frequency of a sound is an increase in directionality—it is difficult to tell where low frequency sounds come from (think of locating a jet plane in the sky!).

The 'biofeed-back' area also began to develop its programme at this meeting and, when we broke up to go our separate ways, content that even a primitive strategy had been developed, I began to wonder about the possible cause of these anomalies. They were so far outside the general run of anomaly reports that, despite any amount of theorising, I felt happy that there were several years of effort ahead—*if* we found anything. It was difficult to predict what might happen if the early monitoring runs found nothing.

THE SONG OF THE STONES

The ultrasonic detector took nearly a year to construct after that initial meeting, and so it was not until mid-October 1978 that I finally received it from Mike Roberts, the Project's electronic engineer. I immediately spent several days familiarising myself with its responses and testing it at many locations near to hand. The first day when I was free to take a dawn reading was Saturday, 21st October, and so, on that dark and foggy morning, I set off for Rollright with my son, then only three, and our large Alsatian for company: the classic team of a man, a boy and a dog.

Driving up the A34 from Oxford, I turned off in the misty dawn, just before reaching the lane to the circle, into the patchwork of back lanes that led to Little Rollright and Chipping Norton. We stopped at several places to take background readings to compare with whatever I found at the circle.

In all these places the detector needle flickered randomly from 0–1 on the 0–10 scale and, from my experience, hastily gained over the last few days, this agreed with the kind of values for the backgrounds obtained around London. Ultrasonics generated by friction and scraping movements like walking through grass, jingling keys and rustling plastic bags, were easy to identify through the brief deflection they produced over and above the background level, and these kinds of interference could easily be eliminated by standing still while taking readings. The detector was screened against audible noise, which gave the advantage of lack of interference from passing vehicles, and it was also screened against the possibility of picking up stray radio transmissions which might produce spurious readings.

We stood at various places in the circle as the mists gradually thinned, and I watched the detector. Apart from the gentle background flicker, nothing happened. After half an hour of this, not really feeling disappointed because I did not know what to expect, we walked across the road and the adjoining field to the hunched and crooked Kingstone which crouched silently in its ring of ugly DOE railings. I switched on the detector and noticed that a regular pulsing movement occurred with the needle. As I looked, I noted down in my book the scale of the pulsing and its periodicity. This was really peculiar in that the pattern was spread over about a minute and then commenced again after about 10 seconds, endlessly repeated.

When at last the cold forced us to move about, I tried different aspects of the stone and found the same phenomenon. By this time, we were all feeling cold, so we went back to the car. Before we climbed inside, I stood in the layby and switched on the detector again: the strange pulsing was still there. I tried several different parts of the layby, then both sides of the road, and still observed the mysterious pulsing.

After drinking some hot coffee and running the car engine and heater long enough to put some feeling back into our frozen feet, we went back into the circle. Here the background was repeated at all points tested, but once back in the layby and around the Kingstone the pulsing was again picked up. It seemed as if the ultrasonic pulsing abruptly 'switched off' as the circle was approached.

The day was warming now and we walked down the lane and along the path to the Whispering Knights dolmen, stopping every so often to record. Even a hundred yards from the layby the detector simply showed the flickering background, and this was repeated all around the collapsed dolmen. By the time we had returned to the Kingstone it was about 9.30 am and the warmth was still increasing—a fine, golden, late October day, silent except for birdsong (which did not affect the detector). When we reached the layby and the Kingstone the pulsation had stopped. Only the background

39

11. Dawn at the Kingsmen: the author monitoring ultrasonics in a chill autumn mist. (Photo: Paul Devereux)

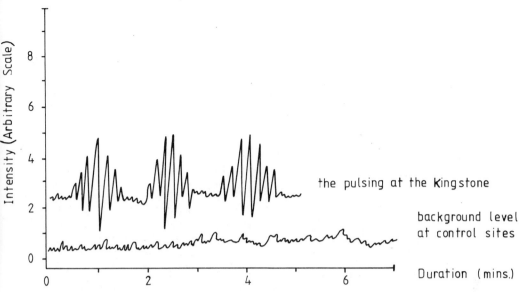

Fig 11. Ultrasound on Day One. The lower line shows the small random fluctuations from the background (e.g. rustling of wind in grass). The regularity of the pulse completely swamps the background fluctuation.

Fig 12. Different Types of Sound Pulse. A pure tone has a regular 'sine' wave, whereas a pure pulse has a distinctive trace like the Rollright signal. The background, as expected, corresponds most to the random 'white noise'.

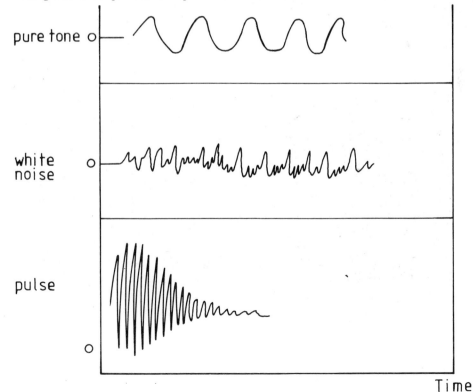

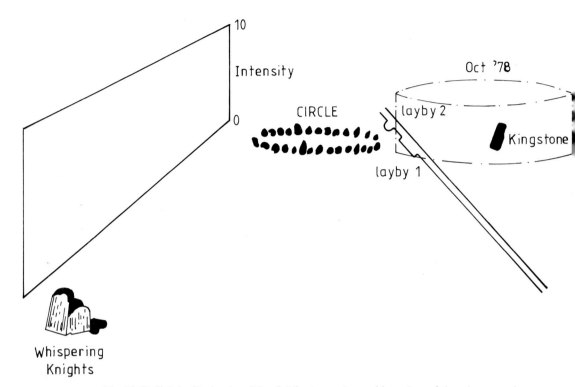

10

Intensity

Oct '78

CIRCLE

layby 2

Kingstone

0

layby 1

Whispering
Knights

Fig 13. Rollright Projection Map I. The intensity and location of the ultrasound pulsing measured in October, 1978.

murmur was observed over the whole of the 'active' region: all around the menhir, the layby, the circle, there was no more pulsing, nothing above the background flicker. I drove down the Little Rollright Lane, stopping at several places and recording, but again found nothing but the background murmur, which hardly flickered above 1 on the scale. There was no pulsing anywhere.

So what was the pulsing? Was it due to the Kingstone or the ground or radio interference, or what? Why had I detected it there and not at the circle? What did it mean?

Compared with the background flickering, it seemed that there was an energy anomaly at the site, but its detection had raised more questions than it answered because of the unexpected *form* of the ultrasonics detected.

As I drove back down the motorway to London I revolved all these questions in my mind, while my young son and the dog slept. Once back home, and all through that afternoon and evening, as I tested and retested

12. Little Rollright Lane, one of the control sites around Rollright for background ultrasonic monitoring. The ridge in the distance is the eastern outlier of the Cotswolds and the distinctive trees around the Kingsmen can be seen on the crest in the centre of the picture.

the detector, always finding the now recognisable background flickering, I slowly began to realise that I *had* found something, whatever it meant or signified, and it happened at dawn. But how had I known to come at dawn?

A STEP IN THE DARK

I had carried out a very simple experiment at Rollright, based upon comparing ultrasonics at the site with the average background in the surrounding countryside. The unexpected and rather staggering success of that experiment had paved the way to more work which would aim at answering the question: is it real?

The events of that morning took a long time to digest, but the follow-up was something for which my own training and experience in scientific

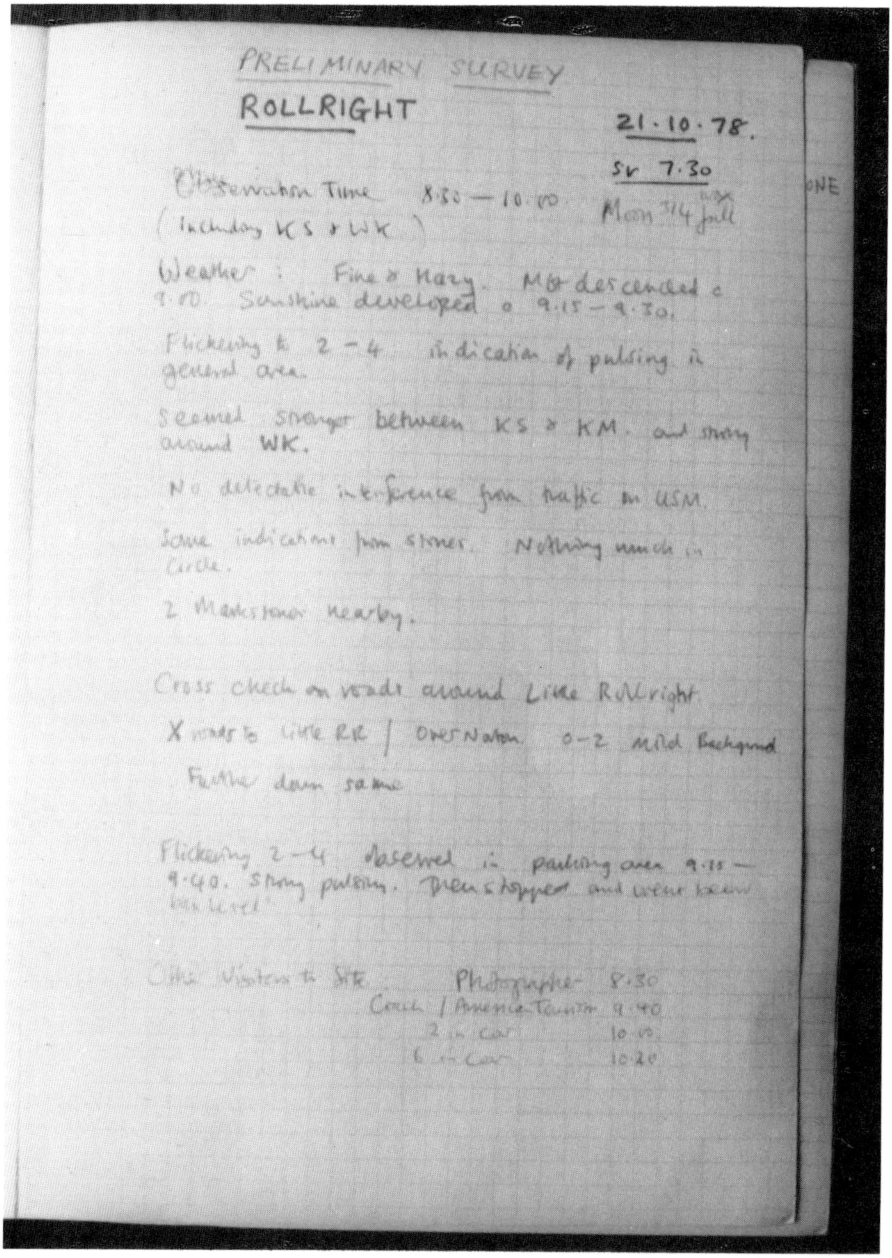
PRELIMINARY SURVEY

ROLLRIGHT

21.10.78.

Sr 7.30

Observation Time 8.30 — 10.00 Moon 3/4 full wax

(Including KS & WK)

Weather: Fine & Hazy. Mist descended c 9.00. Sunshine developed c 9.15 – 9.30.

Flickering to 2 – 4 indication of pulsing in general area.

Seemed stronger between KS & KM. and strong around WK.

No detectable interference from traffic on USM.

Some indications from stones. Nothing much in circle.

2 Markstones nearby.

Cross check on roads around Little Rollright

X roads to Little RR | Over Norton 0–2 Mild Background

Further down same

Flickering 2–4 observed in parking area 9.15 – 9.40. Strong pulsing. Then stopped and went below background level

Other visitors to site: Photographer 8.30

Coach / American Tourists 9.40

2 in car 10.00

6 in car 10.20

research had equipped me. I might be on unknown ground, but I had guides—and guardians.

Research is an evocative word, used very loosely by many people. At one extreme it is one of the highest human activities, at the other it is synonymous with finding out facts from a book or a friend. But real research is Janus-faced. The word itself, '*re*-search', suggests looking back, sifting through information already obtained. In this way it is the work horse of science—where much of the effort, glamorous as it might seem, depends upon a patient, organised search for knowledge and information. But the other face of research is almost a ghost in this faultless cage of logic and method. This is the dark face, the hunch, the intuitive leap in the dark that gives purpose to any scientific endeavour.

The two faces are inseparable. Without the leap of inspiration, any research effort can become a routine factory assembly line working in a value-free desert. Inspiration on its own floats free as thistledown, attaching itself to anything attractive whether it fits or not, and becomes indistinguishable from the flights of fancy so common in this field, where a sufficiently weak body of fact can support *any* free-floating idea.

With one stroke this experiment at Rollright had gone beyond that. Suddenly the Dragon Project had found itself in a position to generate primary data, and on this theories and explanations could be developed. This was going to be the grinding effort spread over years, but it hinged upon that inspirational leap to go at dawn.

During the next few days I took countless background readings around my home in north-west London, even taking dawn readings at a trig. point on Horsenden Hill for comparison. Always I found the background flickering, never that enigmatic pulsing. The pulsing seemed to be the discovery—how big a discovery remained to be seen. *What* it meant was another question, and that could wait. The important task was to generate data, and show that the pulsing could be found again—by anyone with a suitable instrument—to satisfy the terrible twin gods of science, reproducibility and repeatability. If the pulsing could be shown to be a real effect, then we would have succeeded with the Project. The temptation to rush into theories and explanation—so seductive to the amateur researcher—was something I found easy to resist. If the data were real then there would be plenty of opportunity for theories—and speculation.

Firstly, however, I had to make more dawn visits to see if I could pick up

13. Day One of the Dragon Project: the notes recorded by the author in the log book on the first monitoring session, when the ultrasonic pulsing was detected.

45

the start of the pulsing by getting there much earlier. Would I find other parts of the site active, would activity be increased or decreased?

But how had I chosen dawn? What was so special about dawn? The zoologist hadn't mentioned dawn, although he implied some time very early in the morning. To answer this question I had to untangle an intuitive leap, one that depended on a knowledge of some of the stranger properties of rocks and minerals. And, whether the effect was due to the standing stones or the environment itself, stone was there in all of it. For a number of years I had been familiar with some strange features of the inorganic world, and it is to these that we now turn.

3
THE SECRET WORLD
OF STONE

What do you see in that time-touched stone?
When nothing is there
But ashen blankness.
Thomas Hardy, *In the British Museum*

Stone is a byword for hardness and permanence. It seems unchanging, eternal, untouched by time. But below the immutable exterior, subtle forces are at work, and as we go down into its ultimate structure we enter a bizarre, almost living, world.

STONE GIANT

What did stone mean to the megalith builders? Without doubt they had a keen awareness of its obvious properties, such as colour, strength and working qualities. We know that, once a good source of material had been found, trading over long distances took place, and we see examples of such trade routes emanating from bases like the Lake District 'axe factories' and the flint mines of Grimes Graves in Norfolk.

If we look beyond this material awareness of stone to see what it meant to those ancient people, the archaeological record is less clear. How stone might have been worshipped or venerated, how it might have acted as a symbol, we really do not know. All we suppose is that they viewed stone as a symbol of permanence and used it to enshrine something of deep importance to them. It is difficult to go beyond such a vague generalisation, whatever skill and knowledge we think are expressed in the geometry and astronomy of the circles, to say that there was any appreciation of the inner nature of stone.

There are many, however, who maintain that the circles were built with just such an understanding or awareness, and that they are the expression of an ancient science so highly evolved that we can barely recognise it from our more primitive modern level. But to penetrate the surface, to get to the deeper layers of the natural world, we need more than ideas. The range of

47

our senses must be extended to explore these hidden depths, and this we can do most reliably with instruments that function at deep levels of structure and energy where, unaided, we cannot go.

Today, when we look at stone circles in the landscape, we see that the stones are part of their surroundings. Whether locally quarried or drawn from far away, stone is an expression of the landscape in that the visible physical features depend intimately upon the nature of the underlying rock.

The earth itself can be seen as a giant of stone, an inorganic world that we perceive mostly through contact with the stony crust which is some tens of miles thick. Even the inorganic soil derives from rocks and stones, for the most part, worn into powders and fragments. A standing stone, embedded in the earth, is in mute communion with the harsh inorganic world of its birth. The organic world, the soft mutable world of carbon, only intrudes as a thin dusting on this bony crust and a filigree of humus in the soil. It is an

14. The gnarled and weathered limestone of the Kingsmen at Rollright gives no indication of the inner character of the stone at molecular and deeper levels.

1. The Kingsmen Circle at Rollright.

2, 3 & 4. The densely grouped sarsens at Stonehenge (2) contrast vividly with the huge enclosure of Avebury (3) where few stones remain standing. Most British circles, however, are small and obscure, like the Castle Ring near Bakewell in Derbyshire (4. *Photo : Duncan MacNeil*).

5, 6 & 7. The term 'megalith' also embraces stone rows, such as the magnificent Avenue at Avebury (5), burial chambers (or dolmens) like Pentre Ifan (6) and single standing stones, or menhirs, like the Blind Fiddler (7).

ROLLRIG T STONE
KING STONE

NOTICE IS H EBY GIVEN TH T
UNDER THE OVISIONS OF E
ANCIENT M NUMENTS A S
THE MIN ER OF WOR
HAS BEEN CONSTITUTE
GUARDIAN THIS MONUM NT
AND ANY RSON INJUR G
OR DEFAC THE SAME LL
BE LIABLE O PROSECUT N
ACCORDI TO LAW

MINISTRY OF RKS

8. The Kingstone, Rollright, surrounded by its ugly railings.

insubstantial ghost against the vast inorganic stage-set of the earth.

Would the megalithic builders have had this kind of appreciation of the world that lies below the landscape? We do not know, but a realisation of the inorganic nature of our world is a first step in the understanding of stone. Did they ever take the faltering step beyond to ask: what is stone?

THE OXYGEN CAVE

Without sunlight we could not exist, but without the surface of the earth we would have nowhere to live, for all life depends upon the rocks that make up the crust. However deeply we have penetrated the earth we have never gone beneath that crust, and our knowledge of the seething rock below has never been gained directly.

But if we look at the crust we see that three chemical elements—oxygen, silicon and aluminium—account for the greater part of most rocks. Oxygen is paramount, not only accounting for one quarter of the crust, but also for the bulk of the oceans and one-fifth of the volume of the atmosphere. It is the driving force, platform, the fountain of all life on earth.

In the crust it enters into a vast array of combinations with silicon to form the basic structure of the rocks. Silicon dioxide (silica) is the primary building block of the crust. Aluminium oxide (alumina) enters into varying combinations with this in the secondary building block in the form of aluminosilicates. Silica and alumina account for the bulk of the earth's rocks and there are relatively few other rock types which do not include one of these elements. Even if silicon and aluminium are absent, oxygen still provides the framework, as in the carbonate and sulphate rocks such as dolomite, chalk and gypsum, all of which are founded upon oxygen.

In the last two centuries, as the ideas of chemistry and chemical elements were developed, chemical analyses of rocks showed up a complex mixture of oxides based on silica and alumina. These lynchpins were termed 'acidic' oxides and were balanced by the 'basic' oxides of sodium, iron and others to give the total 'neutral' composition of the rocks. Classification could then be made by the relative proportions of the various oxides, and this idea of proportionality was grounded in the first fixed points of chemistry—Dalton's Laws. Substances always have a fixed composition, so it was supposed, although the refinement of analyses showed that there were some uncomfortable exceptions.

Although the early chemists saw rocks as mixtures of oxides, their picture was not wide enough for them to appreciate that this concept was illusory. Their analyses were destructive and their picture of the inner world of rocks was conditioned by the way they had sought understanding within the

49

15. The composite nature of granite, used in the dolmen of Lanyon Quoit, has a complex influence upon its weathering and decomposition. This stone is normally thought to be far more durable than sedimentary rocks such as limestone.

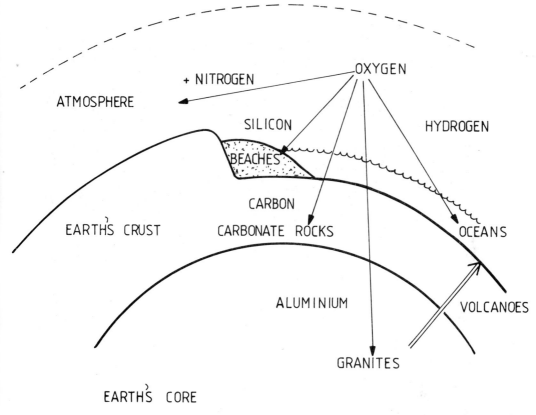

Fig 14. The Oxygen Key. We think of oxygen mostly in connection with the air, but it is the fundamental element of both the earth's crust and water.

analytical technology of their time. This situation was overturned by the sudden advances in science at the end of the nineteenth century, among which was the discovery of X-rays, with their unique and unprecedented penetrating and interactive power.

X-rays opened up a spectacular new way of studying crystals which has since laid the basis of our present understanding of the structure of rock. Most importantly, it put oxygen into its true perspective in the inorganic world. X-rays showed a rigid, ordered world beneath the beautiful but obvious surface of crystallinity. The essence of a crystal is repetition, regularity and order, and this occurs irrespective of its size or shape or its physical appearance. But this order is itself only a reflection of a deeper reality, that of the crystal lattice.

A crystal lattice exists more in our minds than in the crystal. We understand it as the framework of the crystal, and it was quickly found that, in any kind of rock, oxygen provided this framework with a vast geometrical array of atoms extending in all directions, effectively into infinity. Between the oxygen atoms are 'holes' in the lattice—the packing of oxygen atoms providing a honeycomb of caves within which sit the metal ions—silicon, aluminium, sodium, iron and so on. One rock differs from another in the number and type of these metal atoms. Depending on the stacking of the oxygen array, different metal atoms can fit into holes of appropriate size, accounting for the composition of rocks and their acidic and basic character in a very neat and satisfying way.

But not quite. All is not perfect in this rigidly ordered world. Sometimes, metals are missing from their holes, oxygen atoms are displaced, 'intruder' metals may be present, upsetting the overall balance. These subtle deviations give rise to defects, both in the visible crystal and deep within its structure at the atomic level. The defects are the gateways into the ultimate nature of stone.

This strange hidden world is illuminated by 'underground suns' which are the driving force for much of the energetics of stone. They occur in isolated places, in most types of stone, as radioactive elements such as uranium and thorium, that send bursts of energy through the lattice as they decay, some of these causing parts of the cave walls to disintegrate and release electrons from their atoms. The electrons live out their lives in these depths—mostly their lives are very short, but sometimes very long. But they are the lifeblood of the stone, coursing through the depths, constantly being created and consumed, far below the visible crystallinity and structure.

BLOOD OF THE STONE

The electron is one of the strangest things in nature. Of all the atomic particles it is the one that has so far resisted all attempts of nuclear physicists to break it down, but it can actually be generated by the break-up of the nuclear neutron. The electron is the essence of negativity. It packs an enormous negative electric charge (equal but opposite to the much more massive proton) into its tiny frame, although, like a will o' the wisp, it can appear to change from a particle into a wave with bewildering rapidity.

The electron is one of the smallest particles to have an independent existence, and this can last for microseconds or sometimes for thousands or millions of years, depending upon where the electron is. In the stone lattice a newly born electron, split from the cave wall by radiation, faces a range of fierce atomic and molecular predators that have no equal in the biological world. Its strong negative charge and small size make it a tempting morsel

52

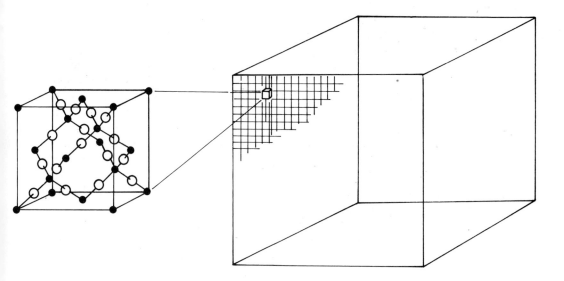

● Silicon

○ Oxygen

Fig 15. The Oxygen Cage. The three-dimensional structure of the rocks is given by the endlessly repeated patterns of the oxygen lattice. Here we see one of the typical silicate packings (orientation of atoms dependent on *size*) in the rocks beneath our feet.

Fig 16. Perfection in Imperfection. The lattice packing of rocks is rarely perfect. Dislocation or absence of particular atoms creates electrical imbalances that give rise to a whole range of interesting electronic effects. These two examples of atomic dislocation are widely exploited by the electronics industry.

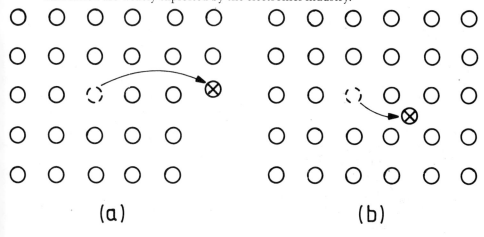

(a) (b)

(a) A Schottky defect (b) A Frenkel defect

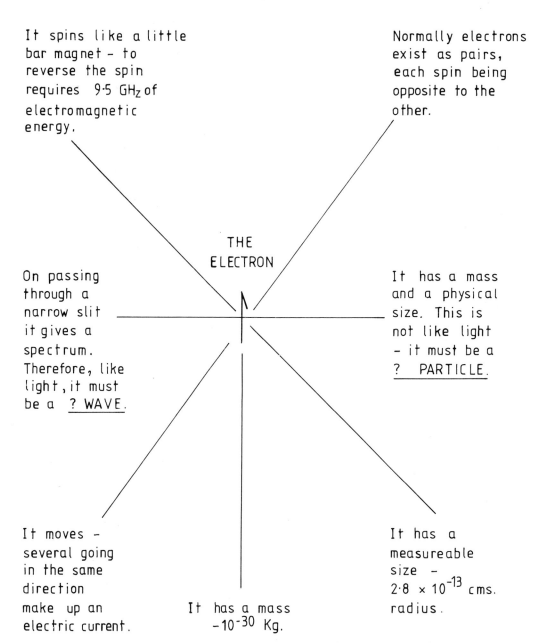

It spins like a little bar magnet - to reverse the spin requires 9·5 GH$_z$ of electromagnetic energy.

Normally electrons exist as pairs, each spin being opposite to the other.

THE ELECTRON

On passing through a narrow slit it gives a spectrum. Therefore, like light, it must be a ? WAVE.

It has a mass and a physical size. This is not like light - it must be a ? PARTICLE.

It moves - several going in the same direction make up an electric current.

It has a mass -10^{-30} Kg.

It has a measureable size - 2·8 × 10^{-13} cms. radius.

Fig 17. The Electron—some of its main features. The measurements of size and mass use the index system to avoid writing a string of zeros (10^{-30} is 29 zeros followed by 1, all *after* the decimal point). The measurements of size and mass, however, depend upon the electron behaving as a particle!

54

for the metallic bases—themselves positively charged—and for any lattice defects which are also positively charged from the loss of electrons. If the electron survives perils of this sort it may escape entirely, or it may tumble into an energy trap hidden in the lattice.

In this strange world, so reminiscent of 'dungeons and dragons', these traps are the weirdest of all. Although associated with the defects, they have no physical reality, existing as energy wells into which the electron falls. The sides are sheer and unscalable unless the electron can find the energy to escape from another source. The easiest way to acquire it is through heat, and the depth of the ghostly trap can be measured in terms of the temperature required to spring the electron out. Many of these traps are shallow and enough heat energy comes from the surroundings to let the electrons escape within minutes or hours. But some are deeper, and an electron can spend

Fig 18. Life and Death of an Electron. When bound into a 'spin-pair', the electron is immobilised. Once it is free it can reach the safe harbour of spin pairing through many bizarre and circuitous routes. We also see how environmental effects (radiation, ultraviolet light, for example) continually create free electrons, replacing those that become captured. When a Geiger counter detects β-rays it detects *electrons*. In radiation these come from atomic nuclei, but without measuring the electron's *energy*, exo electrons and nuclear electrons cannot be distinguished.

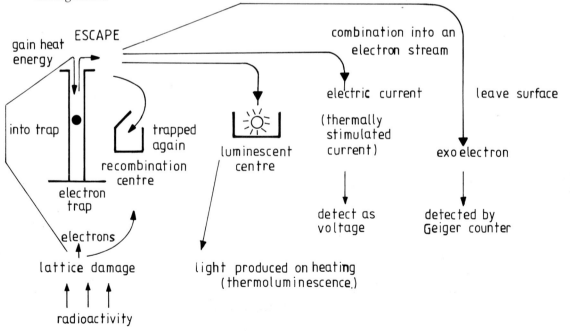

centuries awaiting a fluctuation of heat from the environment to release it. Some are deeper still, and the electron can reside there for countless millennia. An electron is rarely alone. Other electrons tumble into the traps, and since they are all negatively charged and therefore repel each other electrostatically, they are trapped in a gossamer web of these electrostatic repulsions, awaiting the time of their escape.

The traps can only accommodate a certain number of electrons. Over decades, centuries, millennia, the traps gradually fill. The occasional electron falls in, another catches a random energy fluctuation that seeps through the lattice and makes its escape. So we arrive at a system in dynamic equilibrium: given sufficient time the traps will fill and remain filled, but their population will gradually change as some leave and others enter. Free electrons will gradually seep through channels, fissures, cracks, trickling through the caves. Some will perish in the electrical jaws of predators, but the trickle will continue, given enough time.

And time is on its side. The lifetime of an electron, however long it is contained in an energy well, is short when measured against the lifetime of the rocks. A million years are an eyeblink in the life of the oxygen caves, and throughout this time the life cycles of the electrons continue: endless birth, death and rebirth occurring deep in the atomic caverns of the stone, far from sight.

But what has this to do with the megaliths? How can it relate to a deeper purpose for stone, deeper than the surface attributes of placing them carefully in the ground? The answer is intimately connected with the interaction of the electron with its energetic environment.

The electron can interact with energy in two main ways. Free, it has the property of spin and can spin either right or left. Electromagnetic radiation of requisite energy can reverse this spin—the phenomenon called 'spin-flip'; the process will be triggered by microwave energy, and it allows the electron a mechanism to absorb and re-emit energy in this part of the electromagnetic spectrum. When incorporated in an atom or molecule, an electron can jump between energy levels in a suitable molecule, atom or lattice. To do this it needs energy in the visible or ultraviolet region of the electromagnetic spectrum. To jump upwards it requires this energy to be put in, to go downwards it will emit this energy—as light. Added to this, the trickle of electrons through the lattice, however much the population is depleted by natural losses, constitutes the basis for an electric discharge: electrons on the move *are* electricity. The electrons are poised on a knife edge, able to interact with the energy environment, able to combine into an electric current or discharge.

All organic life is based ultimately upon electrons and electricity—the

56

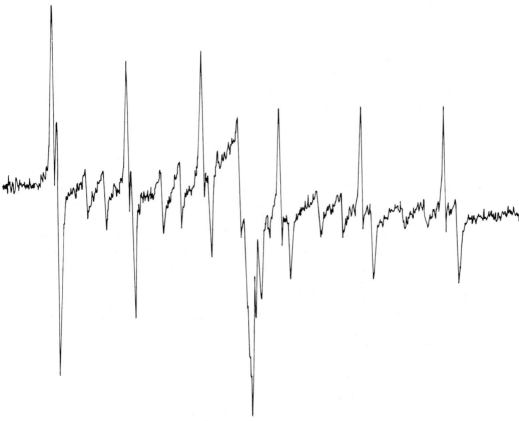

Fig 19. Seeing an Electron through 'Spin-Flip'. In electron spin resonance (esr), microwave energy causes free electrons to reverse their spin. The energy absorption when this happens can be recorded as a spectrum which gives a wealth of information on the energetics of the electron. Here we see the complex spectrum of manganese (a frequent impurity in rock) which normally possesses *five* unbound electrons which coexist without spin pairing in its electron shell. The central lines are due to electrons trapped in defects.

two terms are almost interchangeable—and these electrons also form the life-blood of stone. But electricity only occurs in conductors, where free electron clouds exist, and stone is not a conductor of electricity. It is, nevertheless, a semi-conductor by virtue of this electron population, and only requires triggering, as does any other semi-conductor.

The electrons are the key to living stone. But what else can they do?

THE VITAL SPARK

The electron is the ace in the hole, but trickling through the lattice it plays its single card by becoming receptive to the various sources of energy in its

16. The dense, compacted sandstone called 'sarsen' occurs mainly as scattered blocks and boulders on the Marlborough Downs and these were used by the builders of Stonehenge and Avebury. This huge and jagged sarsen boulder stands in the Kennet Avenue at Avebury.

58

environment. The lattice is not a passive framework, serving only as a reservoir of chipped-off electrons, because it can also respond to its environment in its own ways: at one extreme as an isolated oxygen lattice, at the other as a vast crustal mass of rock in tune with the molten rock tides deep inside the earth.

The key to this interaction is *transduction*—the transformation of energy of one kind into another. One of the earliest transduction mechanisms exploited by man was fire—the conversion of the products of previous photosynthesis into heat. The photoelectric cell—light into electricity—is a more recent example, and its reverse—electricity into light—is the role of the laser. None of these conversion routes are completely efficient, the balance of lost energy being dissipated in 'unstructured' form as heat. Although heat can be converted into other forms of energy—as in turbines—the general tendency is for all forms of energy to degrade to heat, and this has given rise to the concept of entropy and the 'heat death' of the universe.

Our concern with the stone lattice and its trickling electron population is to see how receptive they can be, singly and in combination, to energy coming in from the environment. This receptivity is subtle, not as pronounced as in technological developments where energy input can be controlled for precise uses, but present across a wide energy spectrum, nevertheless.

Stresses encountered by the rocks from crustal movements can be transduced in a variety of ways: minerals such as quartz converting pressure

Fig 20. Electronic Effects. When electrons interact with lattice structures a whole host of effects arises as the energy is rerouted into other forms. Here we see some of these interactions widely exploited in electronic devices but found in many natural materials.

MEDIUM

PRESSURE	TRIBOLUMINESCENCE	LIGHT
	PIEZO ELECTRICITY	
HEAT	THERMOELECTRICITY	ELECTRONS
	PHOTOCONDUCTIVITY	
LIGHT	OPTOACOUSTIC	
	ACOUSTOELECTRICITY	SOUND
ELECTRONS	LUMINESCENCE	LIGHT
	FERROELECTRICITY	
ELECTRICITY		MAGNETISM

waves into electromagnetic radiation in the well-known piezoelectric effect. Frictional stresses, however, can manifest themselves in energy transitions in the electron population, giving rise to visible glows, and this probably accounts for the fantastic 'earthquake lights' associated with faulted regions in the crust. Simply heating rock will drive the electrons pell-mell from their deep traps to emerge either as an electric discharge or as light energy. Sometimes, pushing the electrons into a highly energetic state may leave them there for some considerable time before they lose their energy, and this gives rise to phosphorescence—the ghostly, lingering light that may lie behind the stories of jack o'lantern and the will o' the wisp. In these cases the light comes mostly from the decomposition of organic materials, although the overall electronic phenomenon is the same.

These glimpses into the secret world of stone, the responsiveness of the lattice and its contents to the variations and fluctuations of the energy environment, give us a basis to explore reports of anomalous energies at the stone circles, although we may not be able to distinguish readily between effects due to the circle and those caused by the underlying rock. But this, of course, may not be necessary at first: the priority is to see what is there. Ultrasonic pulsing had been found at the first attempt. Would it be found again? If so, what did it signify, and why was dawn so important?

4
THE DRAGON AWAKES

We cannot but speak the things
which we have seen and heard.
The Acts of the Apostles, iv.20

The long association of the Dragon with some kind of earth force made it a fitting symbol for the quest that began at the Rollright Stones in 1978. The initial success in breaking the silence of the stones now had to be developed before the reality of the legends could be tested.

DRAGON'S PULSE

Two weeks after my first dawn foray, still speculating on the significance of this early monitoring time, I was back at Rollright with my son and dog, armed with the ultrasonic detector. Since my last visit it had been tested at many non-megalithic locations, at all times of the day and night. The pulsing had not been detected anywhere and it was with some trepidation that I returned to Rollright.

The morning was very foggy and so it was actually after dawn when I was driving slowly round the lanes at Little Rollright, making my background checks before reaching the circle.

The background readings hardly flickered above zero and there was no difference at any part of the site. For an hour and a half we tramped backwards and forwards between circle, menhir and dolmen, and up and down the lane, taking readings in the gradually clearing mist. By 10 o'clock it was a brilliant autumn day, the air crystal clear, the low sun adding a mellowness to the autumn scenery that was almost magical. I could imagine Tolkien wandering these lanes—as he surely did at some points—and receiving the inspiration for Lothlorien in this magnificent scenery. We drove around the countryside, stopping by little churches in the brilliant light. Everywhere the readings were minimal. A barely perceptible flicker. No pulsing anywhere.

Had I imagined it that last time? Had I come too late? There was only

61

17. One of the background monitoring sites for the ultrasonic work of the Dragon Project was Horsenden Hill at Greenford in Middlesex. This hilltop, with its trig. point, was monitored on many dawn sessions but the mysterious pulsing was never detected: only random background fluctuations were observed.

one way to tell. I resolved to return at the first opportunity, which would be two weeks later.

Here we come to the crux of the problems associated with this type of work: I had a full-time teaching job and, since the previous year, I had also become more and more deeply embroiled in archaeological science. Our work with trapped electrons in flint had suddenly developed and the publication of a paper in *Nature* was imminent; it was beginning to look possible for me to move into archaeological science full time. I was also in the middle of writing a text book of food science—the subject I taught at college. Where was the time to do it all, and how could I leave anything out?

Two weeks passed, and I had no time free to visit Rollright. A week later the mists had gone but the weather still held. It was clear and very frosty and promised to be another fine day. Determined to be at Rollright well before dawn, I set the alarm for 4.30 and, warmly clad (but never warmly enough), equipped with thermos and detector, I set out, alone this time, in the freezing morning at 5 o'clock, driving swiftly down the deserted motorway to arrive at Rollright at 6.30, one hour before sunrise. Again I stopped in the back lanes for the routine background checks, recording a slight fluttering up to 1 on the scale.

At the circle it was even colder: thick frost, a chill gathering wind, a starlit sky and utter silence. I moved patiently from circle to standing stone to dolmen and to my check points, in the routine I had now established. The background murmured—no pulsing. At 7.10, some twenty minutes before sunrise, I went to the Kingstone and waited silently. Above, the sky was turning blue. The meter continued to show the background flicker until, at 7.15, almost like magic, the pulsing began. Slowly, faintly, the pattern I had seen on my first visit appeared on the dials. This time it was fainter, only reaching 2 on the scale. But it was there!

Fig 21. Rollright Projection Map II. The intensity and location of the ultrasound pulsing measured in November, 1978.

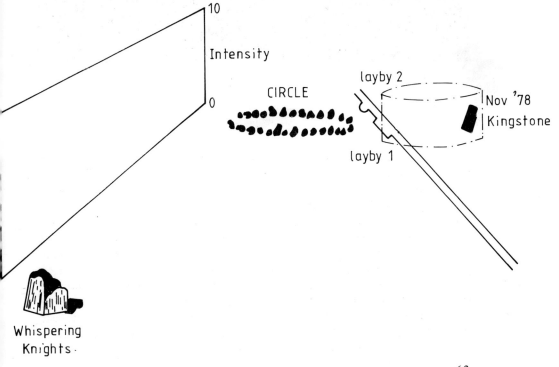

I tried measuring on all sides of the Kingstone and it was there, like an echo of the first morning's attempt. It was apparent in a reduced area in the layby, too, but absent in the circle and the Whispering Knights, as before. I paced my measuring route between the three structures for over an hour while another brilliant day dawned, and I drove around the surrounding countryside taking many control readings, coming back to the circle at 9 o'clock to find that all the pulsing had disappeared and the background had re-established itself at all the measuring points.

I drove back to London and arrived home before my feet had begun to thaw out from the freezing dawn vigil. Cold and exhausted though I was, the strangeness of it all just would not go away. Why had I found nothing on my second visit? Was the pulsing decreasing both in intensity and duration as we approached the winter solstice, so that the previous time I had simply arrived too late? Another predawn visit was called for, soon, and this time I determined that I would concentrate on the Kingstone, where the activity seemed to be focused.

Again, three weeks passed before the next monitoring opportunity arose, on the Sunday before Christmas. The morning was even colder than on the previous occasion. This time I went with Paul Devereux and we sped down the now familiar deserted motorway, the sky lightening over our shoulders as another brilliant dawn approached. We arrived at 7 o'clock, going straight to the circle. The silence and the cold were intense, the sparkling predawn air windless, absolutely still. Background was almost zero, the flickering barely reaching 1 on the scale, with only the slightest fluctuation at all the test sites. We came to the Kingstone at 7.50, some ten minutes before sunrise, and waited in the freezing cold. The sun rose and the detector was not affected, still showing only the faintest flutterings of background.

And then, a few moments after sunrise, the fluttering slowly changed before our eyes. Imperceptibly it changed to the pulsing! Very faint, barely reaching 1 on the scale, but it was there, unmistakably there! We tried all sides of the Kingstone and it was still there, a regular rhythmic pulsing like a faint echo of the first morning. The pulsing was absent this time from the layby, all activity appearing to be concentrated around the Kingstone.

But twenty minutes later the pulse, faint as it was, subsided into the background flickering. The background at the other places was almost imperceptible, and going back to the Kingstone it was difficult to say whether the pulsing had actually faded completely. At all the check points the background was very, very low, but in the circle, when taking the final readings, we noticed something extremely strange: the reading was absolutely zero, without even the slight flutter recorded at the background control sites. How could a reading be *below* background?

9, 10 & 11. The stones of the megaliths.
Massive sarsens guard the entrance to the
West Kennet long barrow (9), while the
pitted limestone figures of the Kingsmen (10)
huddle in the grass at Rollright. The granite
of Lanyon Quoit (11) sparkles in the
afternoon sun.

12. Quiet summer: the Whispering Knights brood in their field as the August sun sets over the Kingsmen in their protecting circle of trees.

13. A dawn monitoring session at the Kingstone. The author is on the extreme right and John Steele, a co-ordinator of the Project, is second on the left. *Photo: Paul Devereux*

14. The weathered stones of the circle at Rollright bask in the sunshine of a late autumn afternoon.

15. Quiet summer. The Kingstone is monitored as the sun sets.

16. Monitoring the Kingstone at dawn for infrared emanations. Archaeologist Chris Stanley looks down on the twisted menhir. *Photo : Paul Devereux*

18. The Kingstone at dawn during a Dragon Project monitoring session. (Photo: Paul Devereux)

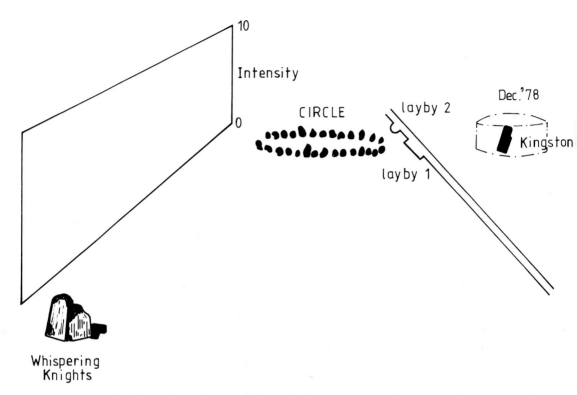

10

Intensity

CIRCLE

layby 2

Dec.'78

Kingston

0

layby 1

Whispering
Knights

Fig 22. Rollright Projection Map III. The intensity and location of the ultrasound pulsing measured in December, 1978.

DAWN THOUGHTS

Ten days later the fine, cold weather finished, and the winter of 1979 began in all its ferocity. For nearly two months all thoughts of Rollright almost disappeared in the mounting chaos of the 'winter of discontent'. But, at odd moments, I fell to wondering about Rollright and the ultrasonics. Had we been approaching some kind of midwinter minimum in ultrasonic intensity, and would we find intensities increasing after the midwinter solstice? On any day that I might have been free to go, the roads were too icy to risk a predawn foray.

But it gave me time to think, although there were too many questions and too few answers. So much was needed to push the work forward, but our resources were very thinly spread—not just resources of money but of time and people as well. All I could think of was to continue the readings, building up a substantial body of data so that we could perceive any underlying trend.

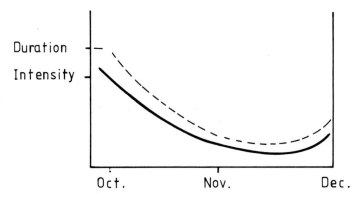

Fig 23. The close correspondence between the duration and intensity of the ultrasonic pulsing in the first sessions at Rollright.

I tried to avoid speculation. There were just so many questions about the ultrasound, that it seemed we must first concentrate upon establishing the reality of the effect before trying to fit it into the megalith builder scenario. But the ultrasonics wouldn't be left alone.

Did they come from the stones or the ground? One test for the future would be either to examine a stone circle built independently in modern times, or to monitor an ancient circle that had been moved 'intact' from its original location. (Both opportunities were later to present themselves.) Why did they come at dawn—were they related directly to the sun, would they climax at the summer solstice? Would we ever find them again? But the question that intrigued me most was how I had chosen to come at dawn.

This notion had come to me one day some time before the first Rollright run, while engaged upon some mundane task. The role of 'absent-minded scientist' is very easy to adopt; over the years—and increasingly as I have become more involved in research activities—I have cultivated the habit, while busy on some trivial job, of encouraging a state of reverie, one that I have found fruitful in producing flashes of insight. The most useful chores to encourage this state are, in my case, dog-walking, car-washing and driving (in that order!). Most research work in the laboratory is then geared, often in long grinding programmes, to testing out these flashes of insight that come and go in a millisecond.

With patient effort the intuitive leap can be laid bare in many cases, and in that cruel winter, there was often time, when stuck in traffic jams in the snow and ice, to ponder over the pieces of the jigsaw.

The key question was where the ultrasonics came from. Whether they came from the standing stones or the ground was not the immediate

67

19. Castlerigg, Cumbria: A Dragon Project monitoring session. This was one of the first occasions when a number of Project members came together at a megalithic site and resistivity measurements were added to the ultrasonic programme. (Photo: Paul Devereux)

problem; what concerned me was *how* they were produced. It was an acknowledged fact, of course, that frictional slipping of crustal faults produced ultrasound, and the circle was near the well-known Rollright fault, but perhaps not near enough to detect anything from it. But why the *pulsing* and why the occurrence at dawn?

Of course, different times of day and measurement on the fault line were also on the programme for 1979, as were many other things, but this was small consolation in that period of frustrating inactivity, while the winter maintained its icy grip through January and February.

Then I realised, very early one morning, while in my garden, that the key could be the sun. Not the sun in the sense of a sunrise orientation, but as a source of electromagnetic radiation. The sun on the horizon is red because the longer wavelength light (the red end of the spectrum) comes straight at us, the shorter wavelengths diffracting away through the atmosphere. We see the sun because the atmosphere has an optical 'window'—light of visible wavelength is let through, more energetic radiation is almost excluded. A small amount of ultraviolet gets through, and if it did not, photosynthesis in plants could not occur. But the more powerful radiations such as X-ray and gamma rays are blocked, which is why X-ray astronomy can only be carried out effectively above the atmosphere.

The atmosphere does have another 'window', in the radiofrequency region, and it is this gap that radioastronomers exploit. But on the edge of this window, just above the infrared region which is almost completely opaque and famous for its 'greenhouse effect', is the microwave region. The sun on the horizon is beaming red light, microwaves and radiowaves at us.

But how did that help? Two things had jogged my memory and pointed the unconscious way. One was that from my own archaeological work I knew that microwaves could 'flip' electrons in a strong magnetic field, but I also knew they could be transduced to pressure waves through a piezoelectric material. The wavelength would stay the same but electromagnetic radiation would become pressure. Push the pressure into the atmosphere and it became *sound*. But the wavelength meant that microwaves would become *ultrasound*.

So, several months after the idea had occurred to me, I stood in my garden at dawn and realised why I had chosen to go to Rollright for dawn readings. It did not matter that limestone, the basic material of the Rollright Stones,

Fig 24. Energy and the Atmosphere. There are two main 'windows' in the atmosphere for visible light and radiowaves. Most of the other radiation (particularly the *hard* radiations such as X-rays) are absorbed before they reach the surface.

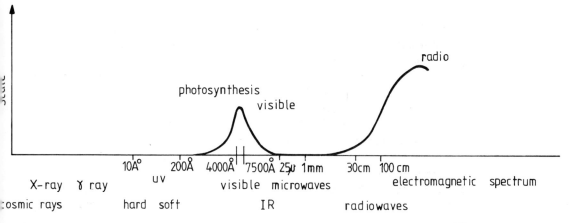

is not a recognised piezoelectric material. It did not matter that the pulsing was unexplained, nor that the influences of time of year, angle of the sun and other similar factors were not considered consciously. Two things had moved me: one, that if it was a microwave effect it should be independent of cloud cover; two, that it gave dawn as the target time. Together they gave me a working hypothesis, a reason to go at dawn that nothing else could. I had a frame of reference, however imperfect, and it was important only in that it would enable me to begin looking at Rollright. The hypothesis is the most important working tool of the scientist. It blunts easily and should be rapidly discarded once it ceases to function, but without it there is often great difficulty in seeing what you are looking for. The real problems come when hypotheses are clung onto despite the facts against them. The facts and observations are always paramount.

I had gone at dawn, probably for the wrong reasons, but I had found the mysterious pulsings. The explanations could come later; my hypothesis was dented but still serviceable. Without it, I might have gone to take readings on Sunday afternoon drives into the country. How many negative runs would have discouraged me from trying again?

SPRING AWAKENING

The winter slackened its grip slightly at the end of February, and the first expedition to Rollright in 1979 was mounted on a grey, cold and overcast day. A number of Project members gathered at the stones some time before dawn, and although other aspects of the Project monitoring were being started up—this was the first proper Project session at Rollright—the ultrasonic monitoring held centre stage.

The predawn backgrounds at the routine checkpoints were higher than before: random fluctuations up to 3 on the scale. As dawn approached I felt myself becoming quite tense. It was one thing to make the solitary dawn run not knowing what to expect; here there was an audience, hoping for a particular result—the very situation I was most anxious to avoid.

Whatever the expectations, they were exceeded. Shortly before dawn, positioned at the Kingstone, I watched the fluctuations in the dreary grey light, and suddenly the fluctuation patterns changed slowly into the regular, rhythmic pulsing! As they did so the intensity gradually increased until there was a full-scale deflection, from 0 to 10. The length and character of the pulsing was just like previous visits—whatever had waned at the solstice was back with a vengeance.

At all points around the Kingstone the activity was maintained at the same level. From the Kingstone to the layby, all along the layby and road,

70

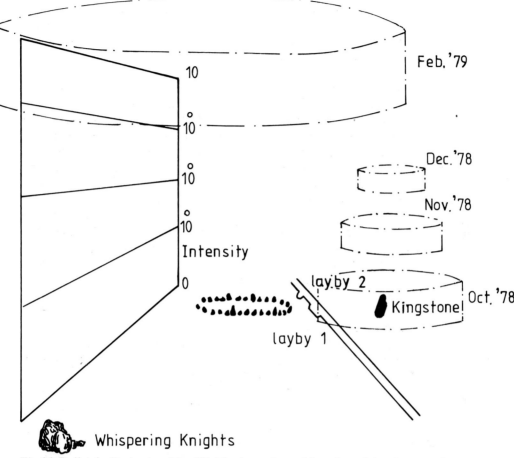

10

$^{\circ}$
10

$^{\circ}$
10

$^{\circ}$
10

Intensity

0

Feb. '79

Dec. '78

Nov. '78

layby 2

Kingstone   Oct. '78

layby 1

Whispering Knights

Fig 25. Rollright Projection Map IV. The intensity and location of the ultrasound pulsing measured in the February, 1979, session at Rollright, compared with the readings from the Autumn of 1978. The impression of a pulsing in space, centred around the Kingstone, as well as a pulsing in time (the form of the observed readings) began to emerge from these initial compilations.

the frantic pulsing was detected. The most surprising observation was to find that the circle and the dolmen also had the same level of activity, and this was true for a considerable distance all around the site. Backwards and forwards we went, the full-scale pulsing evident at all the points, and this went on for over two hours after sunrise. But then the pulsing levels began to decline slowly, and an hour later they slowly faded back into the random fluctuations.

The checks in the surrounding countryside during the whole monitoring period confirmed the overall background levels to be the same as at Rollright. Returning there nearer midday, the random fluctuations were still in evidence at the same levels.

The question now posed was a tantalising one: were we heading towards a summer solstice peak, or was there any real pattern at all? Pattern or not, the feeling that we had a real effect—whatever it meant—grew stronger.

Two more dawn trips in the following month, one two weeks later and one just before the equinox, again showed surprises. The intensities declined each time. They were still strong but lower than the February readings. As the intensity declined, so did the duration of the effect decline from the three-hour span seen in February. This agreed with the observations made at the end of the previous year, although they had not drawn comment then. Plotting graphs of intensity against date and time led us to predict that the readings might vanish in midsummer, which suggested that the October readings could have been declining from the high point in the autumn equinox.

We had replaced one mystery—the anecdote of ultrasound at an ancient site—with a host of deeper ones. Not the least of these was the observation at the equinox that the intensity levels in the circle were exceeding those around the Kingstone. In all these spring monitoring sessions the circle was active ultrasonically, which contrasted dramatically with the quietness noted at the end of the previous year. There was also the impression that the extent of the active area increased in line with the increase in ultrasonic intensity and its duration, and this area seemed to be centred upon the Kingstone. At some point in this ebbing between the spring equinox and the summer solstice, would we see the activity fade from the circle? This exciting possibility now started to guide our monitoring schedules: we were ourselves making a transition from recording the phenomenon to predicting its course.

QUIET SUMMER

Through April and May the level and duration of the readings did continue to decline. We were obviously not heading for a solstice maximum; the peak of activity around the equinox more and more suggested a solstice minimum. These results didn't square with the idea of the sun sparking off the ultrasonics, since, on that premise, we would expect a midsummer peak and a midwinter low. By the sun hypothesis, of course, we were thinking of a

20. The author monitoring the circumference of the Kingsmen circle with a 40KHz (narrow band) ultrasonic detector. (Photo: Paul Devereux)

21. Part of the northern perimeter of the mighty ditch and embankment at Avebury. Ultrasonic pulsings similar to those recorded at Rollright were observed at this point during the dawn monitoring session.

74

reaction with the stones giving rise to the ultrasound. Perhaps it was not the stones but the site itself? The high February readings seemed to be very general all around the site, whereas the low solstice readings seemed to be in a restricted area, around the Kingstone, and the decline in level and duration observed seemed to confirm this early opinion.

We now had a dilemma with the Project logistics. The limitations of the number of instruments available, their capabilities and the available time of the Project members meant that choices had to be made. Obviously we wanted more instrumentation with greater refinements. Our sturdy detector, although very sensitive, was limited in performance and recording ability—there had been no point in constructing an elaborate and sophisticated machine for such a problematic exercise, so we could hardly complain about its inability to cope with the present demands of the Project. Mike Roberts then undertook to construct a more sophisticated machine, one, moreover, which would be able to modulate the ultrasonic signal to audible sound. This opened up exciting possibilities of listening to the 'music of the stones', with overtones of *Close Encounters* and *2001* to stir the imagination. Many problems developed in the construction of this instrument, which was finally brought to fruition several years later.

That early spring of 1979 was an exhilarating time: the pattern seemed to be emerging in the ultrasound, and we finally raised money to buy ourselves a rugged Geiger counter and begin measurements at Rollright. In this, we were extremely fortunate in making contact with an interested local resident who agreed to take a whole range of readings for us. One day, Paul Devereux was at Rollright on another aspect of the project work and, as usual during normal hours, he attracted some attention from visitors. One of these was a local man, Roy Cooper, who lived in Woodstock, some ten miles down the road towards Oxford, and who had relatives living around Rollright who knew the area intimately. He offered to take a series of readings for us and his technical training gave us complete confidence in his ability to use the ultrasonic detector and Geiger counter. This was an absolute boon to us, as the strain of the weekly or fortnightly visits was beginning to tell, and the possibility of accumulating a large group of readings in a very short space of time was very attractive.

So the picture began to fill out. The gradual decline of the ultrasonics towards the solstice and rise towards the equinox was confirmed during the second yearly cycle with the ultrasonic monitoring, but the Geiger counter readings failed to yield anything of interest; a range of places was measured around Rollright and, although variations were noted, these seemed to be no more than would be expected with any monitoring session, since the average count stayed fairly constant. Disappointing as these results were, the

75

positive side of the exercise was the building up of a detailed picture of Rollright with the counter, which stood us in good stead when this area of the Project came alive.

Two additional experiments were tried with the ultrasonic detector away from Rollright, to try to answer the increasingly important question: were other circles active? Paul Devereux took the detector to Castlerigg in Cumbria in December 1978, and I went to Avebury in May 1979. A dawn reading was obtained at Castlerigg—the same pulsing, very faintly, but somewhat stronger than in December at Rollright. In May the Rollright readings were declining rapidly and so I chose a bright, warm morning to head for Avebury, arriving at 5.30 a.m. I checked the background in the West Kennet Avenue and found fluctuations up to 1 and a similar background around the ditch of the giant outer circle. Just at sunrise, the small fluctuation developed into the pulsing! It was there, up to 3 on the scale, and it lasted for some 20 minutes before fading to the background fluctuation. Avebury is too big to cover adequately in a short space of time, so I just stayed where I was, watching the pulsing.

Later, when it had finished, I went up onto the Downs, taking background readings at many different places, including among the Grey Wethers—the groups of huge sarsens deposited on Marlborough Down by glacial action millennia ago and used as the quarry for both Avebury and Stonehenge. At one point I found an isolated group of stones that formed a rough, recumbent circle. This showed the same kind of background and could constitute a control of sorts, although on this occasion it was well past dawn. The site was earmarked for further measurement.

I went back to the circle and found that the background fluctuation had re-established itself, then I retraced my steps down the stone avenue, finding the same levels. Going between the stones in the stone avenue I noticed that the background seemed subdued, reaching about 0·5 rather than 1. I went in and out of the stone avenue at various points and the slight difference was still there.

Twice now a below-background reading had been obtained. Later that summer Paul Devereux found another one at Moel-ty-Uchaf in the Berwyn Mountains in North Wales. The puzzling thing about these 'anomalies within anomalies' was that it was difficult to think of a spurious source of the readings. With the pulsings, one had to be constantly on guard against

22. Ultrasonic monitoring in the Stone Avenue at Avebury produced the first clear observation of an anomalous 'low': while pulsing was not detected, the level of random fluctuations inside the avenue was *below* the background levels recorded outside.

23. Geiger counter monitoring in the Dragon Project. The author taking measurements at Moel-ty-Uchaf in the Berwyn mountains in mid Wales, where a very interesting pattern of variations in count-rates emerged. (Photo: Paul Devereux)

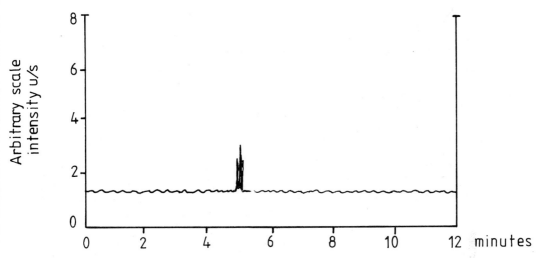

Fig 26. Signing Off. An example of the single sunset pulse at Rollright.

this possibility, although so far the obvious contenders, and many less obvious ones, had been eliminated. We had no framework to contain these anomalies, and they just sat in the log books, begging questions.

Two other pieces of the jigsaw were slotted in by Roy Cooper's efforts: daytime readings at Rollright failed to find any pulsing. Evening readings, which might conceivably have mirrored dawn on the 'sunrise hypothesis', were blank except for a few isolated pulses noted around the time of sunset, almost as if the site were 'signing off'.

The Geiger counter produced nothing out of the ordinary and the fine summer slid away, the pulsings noted on the ultrasonic detector fading into background fluctuations. Where did we go from here?

There were many possibilities. One was to leave the physical monitoring at this stage and develop the 'human interaction' side of the Project. Another was to raise funding for a massive round-the-clock effort at the next equinox maximum, although we would have to aim at Spring 1980 to give us time to organise. This we decided to do, and so Operation Merlin was born—the first 'mass assault' on a stone circle. We would do the physical monitoring, human interaction, everything, if we could raise the money to buy equipment and pay people's expenses to stay at the circle in the hut. It was an exciting possibility, if we could get our act together in time for February 1980.

79

24. Roy Cooper, the Dragon Project anchorman at Rollright, during one of his many patient sessions of Geiger-count monitoring at Rollright. (Photo: Paul Devereux)

17. The Four Stones at Radnor. Legend says that every night they walk to the nearby pool to drink.

18. Stonehenge: water used to wash the stones was reputed to have healing virtues.

19. One of the Pipers, near Buryan in Cornwall, said to have enticed the Merry Maidens to dance one Sabbath evening. For this, they were all turned to stone.

20. Lichfield Cathedral, said to embody cabalistic geometry in its construction. It stands on a prehistoric site. *Photo: Duncan MacNeil*

22. Moel ty Uchaf, in the Berwyn mountains of Wales. This infrared photograph enables us to see the 'invisible' circle only through the use of colours our eyes can detect. We cannot respond directly to infrared radiation with our sense of vision. *Photo: John Steele*

Opposite
21. The focus of ancient wisdom? The Sphinx broods before the Pyramids at Giza.
Photo: Richard and Helena Jaeschke

23. Many mediaeval churches
have traces of earlier
religions and cultures: this
unusual carving looks out to sea
from the church of Madron in
Cornwall.

24. Wayside crosses, common in
Cornwall, probably sanctify
remnants of ancient religions.

5
ECHOES OF THE PAST

When norsemen heard thunder
Did they really believe
Thor was hammering?
W. H. Auden, *Archaeology*

Any new idea on the circles often draws upon legend and folklore for support. Few come away disappointed, because the kaleidoscope of myth and legend shows any pattern that is looked for, so confusing and fragmentary is the material. What will we find when there are no preconceived ideas, only the results of a bizarre experiment at a stone circle? What does the past have to say about the circles?

WORD OF MOUTH
The silence of a stone circle is that of the hurricane's eye, for streaming around it is a vast cloud of spoken tradition, voices from the past. Myth, legend, superstition: these stories speak of the origins of the circles, strange properties of the stones, perhaps fragments of ancient ceremonies, and many of the tales are enshrined in the striking and colourful names attached to circles, menhirs and dolmens.

What can we make of these legends? Do they really speak of the original purpose of the circles, or are they overlaid with so many other myths and folk tales of later times that any early tradition is unrecognisable? Many of the more orthodox take this view, dismissing the traditions out of hand as mere rustic superstition, the product of ignorance or credulity. Others, sober but less extreme, find that many of the names of the stones are so striking (perhaps the most striking thing about them!) and so evocative of past ceremonies or customs, dimly remembered, that they accept that there may be some substance in these traditions, however bizarre they might seem.

The unorthodox take folklore to their collective bosom: the sheer strangeness of the legends, their hints of magic and elder religions, point to a distant memory of an ancient science used to build the circles, and to a

25. Long Meg and her Daughters, one of the many famous megalithic groups said
to be people turned to stone. This recurring motif may simply relate to the
evocative shapes of the stones, or it may hark back to earlier religious practices that
provoked the wrath or hostility of an ascendent Christianity. (Photo: Duncan
MacNeil)

82

mysterious 'earth energy'. This secret science was never wholly lost but deteriorated into witchcraft, a toy for the ignorant or decadent of later ages who pursued the rituals with no real knowledge of their true meaning. From this viewpoint, the broadcasting in the 1960s of the astronomical and geometrical properties of the circles could be seen as the rediscovery of a visible remnant of this ancient and secret science.

The silence of the stones does not deny any of these ideas, however wishful or far-fetched. We are, however, left wondering over the major question: how likely is it that any record of those times has been transmitted in a recognisable form over at least three and a half thousand years? While others have shown that the survival of the spoken word is not something to dismiss lightly, we still have to wonder how much would survive the constant waves of invasion that swept through Britain up until mediaeval times: through Bronze Age Wessex, the Iron Age Celts, Romans, Saxons, Danes, Normans. And even after this layering of competing, conflicting and overwhelming cultures, we have to take into account the devastating effect on rural life of the eighteenth century enclosures and the flight to the cities in the Industrial Revolution—not to mention the wholesale destruction of the mediaeval population by the Black Death in the intervening period.

Fig 27. The Waves of Invaders in Britain. How can the memories of the circles and their purpose survive this overlaying and intermingling unscathed?

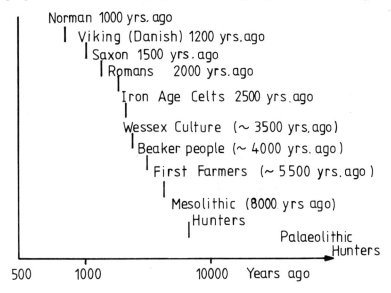

The odds are undoubtedly stacked heavily against old traditions coming through in a recognisable form, even if any such ceremonies were open to common gaze. Suppose they were secret, like the Eleusinian mysteries—would we then expect their substance to survive as a vague tradition? There is one thing in favour of some kind of survival, however, and that is the presence of the 'eternal peasant' in any rural landscape.

We may presume that a wave of invaders, whether peaceful or warlike, will always coexist with some proportion of the native population. Warrior aristocracies, as typified by the Wessex chiefs and Norman lords, needed a docile peasantry to maintain their agricultural economy and could best use and adapt the one already established at the time of their arrival. In this way it is possible that, despite successive waves of invasion and conquest, a dwindling remnant of earlier peoples survived; diluted and mongrelised maybe, but keeping a residue of their beliefs and traditions which still showed through the layers brought by the later peoples, however much it was merged and changed and reinterpreted.

We can never know the answer to these questions because there is too little information, too little fact. As with the legends of early Britain embellished and reported by Geoffrey of Monmouth, we may argue, interpret, reinterpret, but we get no nearer the truth. The few statements that seem plausible must be seen against the backdrop of many others that we dismiss because we cannot accommodate them. Yet who is to say which is correct—the stories we agree with or the ones we reject? Equally, how do we decide which legends might have something to say about the bizarre energy anomaly uncovered at Rollright? Let us have a look at some of them.

TURNED TO STONE

The Rollright legend, of a king and his followers turned to stone, is one of the most striking and yet common among stone circles. The Merry Maidens, the Hurlers, Stanton Drew, Long Meg and her Daughters, all are associated with traditions that they are petrified people. The commonest theme has a religious undertone: the stones are people who were petrified for dancing or enjoying themselves on the Sabbath. Rollright differs from this and it also has a most complex legend of petrifaction: an army and its leader were turned to stone by a witch, becoming the Kingsmen Circle and the Kingstone. The collapsed dolmen is the five Whispering Knights, petrified where they hung back behind the army, whispering treason among themselves against the King. Stories of people being turned to stone are universal, but in Britain the legends are tangible, clustered around the standing stones, and the breaking of the Sabbath places these extant legends in Christian times rather than the Bronze or New Stone Ages. Perhaps we need to look no further than the resemblance of standing stones to motionless figures? A quick-witted cleric may have devised a cautionary tale to keep his erring flock from the attractions of secret pagan ceremonies at the stones.

Christianity was hostile to the older religions, but the general policy was to build churches in or at pagan shrines in order to wean the population gradually onto the new God. Almost up until modern times, however, a constant stream of edicts and admonishments has seemed to be necessary to deter the people, particularly in the remoter country districts, from association with the old religions at the stones. But while churches were built on holy hills and shrines, they were not normally sited inside the circles. Mostly these were shunned, falling outside the general embrace that took in other pagan places. Even at Avebury, where the mediaeval village straddles the stone rings and giant embankments, the church lurks rather self-consciously outside.

Whatever religion the Church was opposed to, and whether or not its ceremonies involved dancing at the stones, we cannot say that it was a Stone Age relic, or even perceived to be a continuation of a very ancient practice. In mediaeval times Roman Britain and the formation of Saxon England were matters of legend, lost in the mists of antiquity. Direct knowledge of still earlier times was probably even more tenuous. The remote past began where living memory ended, and spoken traditions, even when handed down through generations, were difficult—have always been difficult—to fix in time.

But to return to Rollright. The complex story of the confrontation between the army and the witch does not fit the religious picture very easily. Perhaps it refers instead to a genuine tradition of a past battle and a defeated army? There are a number of possible contenders—the Romans were militarily active in the Cotswolds of which Rollright forms an eastern outlier, and Danish armies were defeated in nearby Wessex in the time of Alfred. In more recent times the Civil War came to Edgehill, near to Rollright. The name attached to the dolmen, however, suggests that it was fixed in mediaeval times, although this could be a more recent accretion or variation on an earlier legend related to an army.

The evidence of folklore is plastic—it can be moulded around any suitable theory. Or it can be dismissed because not all its elements fit such a theory. Maybe there is more: perhaps the underlying and persistent allusion to witches is significant, giving a clue to the threads of an earlier religion associated with the circles, even though it may not go back to their origins. We shall explore this problem in Chapter 6. There are, however, some even stranger legends associated with the stones, which are worth investigating.

85

26–29. The Rollright Legend. Among the most detailed and colourful of the petrifaction legends is the one attached to the Rollright complex. It tells of a King and his army who were crossing the county when they encountered a witch just below the ridge. The witch said that if the King could take seven long strides and then see the village of Long Compton over the ridge, he would become King of England. The challenge seemed so easy that the King began the seven strides with complete confidence, while his army looked on and his knights hung back whispering conspiracy against him. As he reached the crest, the 'archdruid's barrow' blocked his view on the seventh stride and he, his knights and army were turned to stone by the witch who, at the same time, turned herself into an elder tree.

And so they stand, turned to stone to this day. The hunched Kingstone rests just below the crest (26), the view of Long Compton forever beyond his gaze (27). The army of the King's men stands behind the King (28), frozen into immobility, while the five treacherous knights (29) still huddle in their whispering conspiracy.

86

87

STONES THAT WALK

Some kind of rationalisation of the petrified people legends can be made, even though there are many loose ends and probably no direct link with the builders of the circles and their beliefs. Other legends are not so tame.

Underlying many of the petrifaction legends is a persistent theme that on certain days the stones move. The Rollright Stones walk to a nearby stream to drink, and other stones rotate on their axes.

Walking *on* water has a famous precedent, but what of walking *to* water? It is again tempting to dismiss these stories out of hand, so superficially absurd do they seem. But could there be a basis, however distorted by tradition, in religious ceremonies, or in something to do with the location of the circles?

We might take the view that the circles simply epitomise the importance of water to primitive farmers, and that the legends perpetuate this significance. Would it not, however, be more appropriate to invoke a holy well, or even a rain god, rather than a stone circle? Moreover, the water should surely come *to* the circle, unless the shape of the circle represents a drop of water!

Less prosaic attitudes draw on a wider spectrum of evidence, but many hinge on the belief that circles are located above the crossing points of underground streams and water courses and draw a connection between the two. Again, the idea of earth energy raises its head—does the movement of the stones give a clue to this mysterious science? Is it the stones that move, or the energy?

Whichever way we look, nothing seems to fit tidily. Perhaps our biggest problem lies in expecting folklore to provide evidence about the original use of the circles. The demonstration of dancing ceremonies may exist only in the eyes of the beholder, rather than in the past—certainly in the more remote past of the circle builders. Perhaps the strongest evidence is the fact that it *exists* rather than that it tells of a particular series of events.

TOUCH OF MAGIC

Beneath the legends of petrified people and walking stones lies a fine mesh of tradition that tells of the way the stones themselves interact with people. Contact with the stones, in a certain way and at a particular time, is said to ensure health, good fortune or fertility. Other legends are darker— interference with the stones will call down retribution from mysterious gods or 'guardians'. So powerful is the spell of some of these prohibitions that they have undoubtedly saved some of the megaliths from destruction in historical times. These tales are coupled with related traditions of

30. Churches were sometimes built within henges but never, seemingly, when a stone circle was there first. The mediaeval church at Avebury is a good example of this reluctance to approach the stones: while the village straggles across the henge the church looks over the enormous enclosure from outside.

movement—stones may not resist removal but will often secretly return to their original setting under cover of night. Other stones strongly resist removal, acting malevolently on those who would try to shift them.

The advocates of the circles as focuses for 'earth energy' naturally claim that these legends amply support their case. The tapping of this energy for beneficial influences has to be carefully controlled, otherwise disaster may ensue; even in their present ruinous state the circles are still said to be the site of considerable latent forces. Alternatively, we may see the accent on fertility as a reflection of primitive man's obsession with procreation: hunter, gatherer, farmer, all are concerned with the fertility of plants and animals, and, of course, of the people themselves. It is more difficult to fit healing into this scenario unless we invoke an associated religion that included healing, such as witchcraft or shamanism. Even then, these traditions do not necessarily lead us back into the Stone Age: the major preoccupations of a farming community would have been the same at any point, from the first farmers up to relatively modern times. With the moving stones we have a problem similar to that posed by the walking stones. Perhaps it was a grim story put around by adherents of the old religion to counteract the Church's propaganda amongst the wavering peasantry. Perhaps it was a tradition generated by accidents caused by clumsy attempts to destroy megalithic structures. We cannot tell.

Or *could* it be earth energy? Are these stories and traditions really reflections of a lost knowledge, or simply of encounters with the circles by later peoples who realised that something strange lurked below the surface and immortalised their fears in striking and imaginative stories? Certainly we do not need continuity with the Stone Age to make this explanation feasible. And yet there are many megalithic sites that have served as a focus for Arthurian legend, and many others are described simply as the work of the Devil. How are we to know which stories, if any, are real, and how do we know if there is any substance behind the tales of an ancient and mysterious science expressed in the building of the circles?

Our strange revelations at Rollright made no distinction between an effect coming from the site and one coming from the stones, and they could not say whether it was caused by an interaction of the two. If there really is a touch of magic—some ancient understanding that has been lost—what evidence for it survives today? What ancient science could have existed that has eluded the archaeologist's spade?

90

6
PHILOSOPHER'S STONE

Our intellectual marines
Landing in little magazines
Capture a trend.
  W. H. Auden, *Under Which Lyre*

Behind the legends of the stones some discern a strange and distant world built from an ancient science that we can now scarcely comprehend, whose fragments survive in the associated traditions of magic. Was this time truly a golden age—a scientific Garden of Eden now lost to us forever—or does the distance of time lend an enchantment only to those who wish to see it?

PAST PERFECT

The past really *is* secure. Whatever happened in megalithic times cannot be altered, although our understanding of those days, and the purpose of the circles, is coloured both by the available evidence and by the way we would like those times to have been.

We view the past, of course, with the advantage of hindsight. We know what came before the megaliths and what came after, and the long perspective of centuries lets us detect patterns in human endeavour that those living at the time could not perceive. On the other hand, passing fashions and ideologies may cause patterns to be imposed on events, and while this manipulation of history has a sinister side to it, there is also a more attractive aspect—the idea that at certain times conditions came together to produce a 'golden age'.

The concept of a golden age seems to respond to a deep human need. Almost every culture looks back to a time when things were simpler, innocent, perfect, and when peace and harmony reigned. We can see this yearning for a golden age manifested as nostalgia for the Victorian and the early twentieth century periods that are inexhaustively portrayed as TV dramas. But the golden age can be detached from any link with a known reality, and the edges blurred until it almost equates with mythology—itself

91

a potent source of golden age tales—as in the film fantasies of the *Star Wars* genre and the burgeoning 'sword and sorcery' literature derived from the Tolkien sagas.

All these golden ages, wherever they are located, in the past, the future or in pure fantasy, have one thing in common: we know that they are doomed. A threat hangs over them and although the characters may survive the hammer blows of fate—war, cataclysm, pestilence—their idyllic existence will be shattered. This isolation, the impending doom, makes a golden age a receptacle for a vast range of almost intangible longing. Why this should be so we do not yet understand.

And so back to megalithic times. They share common attributes with other golden ages, not least their abrupt cessation with the blossoming of the Bronze Age. The archaeological record of the Bronze Age, with its weapon-led technology and cults of the hero and warrior chief, provides the evidence of the first really organised effort in war and defence which opened the floodgates for an ever-spiralling sophistication and savagery in warfare that has characterised Europe ever since. It is very tempting to look back beyond the ages of metal and see the circles as the focus of a golden age that perished beneath the juggernaut of metallic technology. Some have looked beyond the immediate megalith builders and claimed to see signs that link them to an ancient high civilisation with an advanced but unobtrusive technology, a civilisation that had moved beyond war and weapons—in fact an archetypal golden age that is inevitably linked to Plato's Atlantis. These ideas allow our accepted view of man's progression through the archaeological phases to be turned on its head. Instead, we see an accelerating decline from a highpoint in remote antiquity, and, we are told, if we look about us with eyes that can see, we can still observe the traces of that civilisation, its outlines shimmering ghost-like beneath the accretion of the ages determined by orthodox archaeology. The traditional view of the archaeological evidence tells us otherwise: that there is only an onward technological advance throughout mankind's existence on earth. Let us see if there is any evidence to reconcile these unorthodox views.

ANCIENT KNOWLEDGE

Our world picture is one of continued and accelerating progress, and this view is reinforced by the perspectives afforded by archaeology. Looking back down the centuries and millennia, through to the times of the first hunters, then the first true humans, into the twilit world of the pre-humans where ultimately the earliest creatures that we liken to humanity merge with the geological record, we see a frantic, clawing ascent towards our own time.

92

31. The electronic wizardry of Maxwell Cade's 'Mind Mirror'—which monitors changes in brain wave patterns—in use at a session in the Kingsmen circle as part of the human interaction, or 'software' programme of the Dragon Project. In this way, any influence of the site upon the observer can be examined and such work may well pave the way for an appreciation of ancient people's perception of the qualities of these sites which physical monitoring on its own will not yield. (Photo: Paul Devereux)

The evolution of technology, from the first grasped stick and the first fire, through the chipping of flint, to the winning of metals, up to our own technological age, shows us mankind striving ever upwards, although towards what we do not know, since all utopias seem to turn to ashes when they are grasped.

It has been said that this thirst for knowledge, this desire for mastery over the environment, which is so characteristic of western cultures, has been gained at the expense of wisdom. Other societies, which have rejected or never sought to attain this technological path, are said to have evolved a greater level of wisdom, and in recent years many authors have tried to show that this ancient wisdom has anticipated our most advanced knowledge.

How, then, should we see the construction of the circles—as the product of an ancient science and technology, as an ancient wisdom, or both? Certainly, the circles were the product of some kind of knowledge, but can we say they reflect a science or wisdom in advance of our own?

When we look at the past with archaeological eyes we see the remains of ancient technology most clearly. Archaeology can tell us about the materials of the past, but it has less to say about aspects of ancient life that leave no tangible record. This gulf between the visible remains of an ancient people and their intangible human qualities becomes progressively harder to bridge the further back we go in time, because the material remains become sparser, reflecting more and more primitive technology, and this in turn yields less and less human information. At the earliest sites, associated with the emergence of mankind, the main debate is often over fragments of stone or chipped pebbles or fractured bones, and whether or not they actually provide evidence of a simple technology.

How, then, does the impressive technology so much in evidence at megalithic sites argue for the existence of an ancient science, wisdom or both? Do we even need to invoke an ancient science to explain the construction and siting of the megaliths, when during most of recorded history we have seen technology existing quite happily without science? Our present concept of science and its relationship with technology is a very recent one and does not stretch very far back towards the dawn of modern science, in the Renaissance. For most of the time modern science has either been led by technology—the explosive growth of technology in the

Fig 28. The Megaliths in Perspective. We normally perceive the past as an accelerating technological race towards our present level, and this view depends upon seeing humanity gaining an increasing domination over the material world. The building of the circles is seen as just one technological highpoint among many others, although the *reason* for building them can only be ascribed to a demonstration of technological prowess if this perspective is adopted.

94

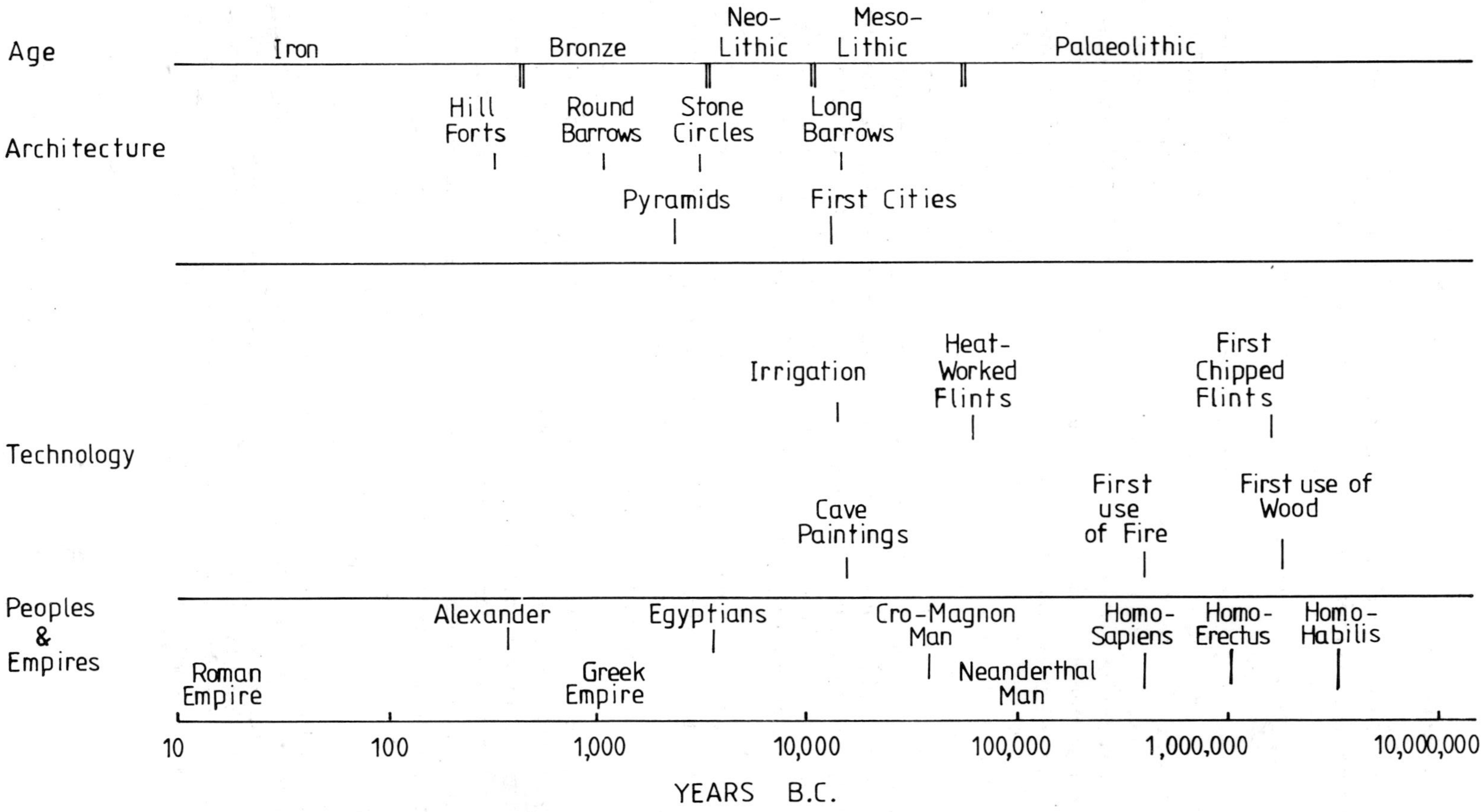

This is a timeline chart plotting developments across four categories against a logarithmic scale of YEARS B.C. (from 10 to 10,000,000).

Age (top row, left to right):
Iron — Bronze — Neo-Lithic — Meso-Lithic — Palaeolithic

Architecture:
- Hill Forts
- Round Barrows
- Stone Circles
- Long Barrows
- Pyramids
- First Cities

Technology:
- Irrigation
- Heat-Worked Flints
- First Chipped Flints
- Cave Paintings
- First use of Fire
- First use of Wood

Peoples & Empires:
- Roman Empire
- Alexander
- Greek Empire
- Egyptians
- Cro-Magnon Man
- Neanderthal Man
- Homo-Sapiens
- Homo-Erectus
- Homo-Habilis

Scale (YEARS B.C.): 10 — 100 — 1,000 — 10,000 — 100,000 — 1,000,000 — 10,000,000

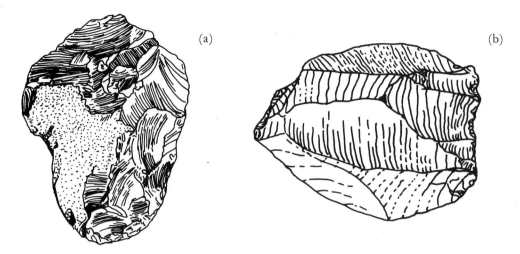

Fig 29. (a) an 'Eolith'; (b) an Early Flint Tool. The earliest traces of man's technology are 'eoliths' or 'dawn stones' which are said to be crudely chipped to give working edges. Such chipping is difficult to distinguish from frost and mechanical fracture of unworked flints, but quite different from the flaking of even early palaeolithic tools. It is not easy for an untrained eye to distinguish an 'eolith' from a naturally fractured pebble. (*Drawing by Eileen Barnes*)

Industrial Revolution and the mediaeval development of firearms and cannons generated exploration in many areas of science that laid the foundations of the modern disciplines—or by the need to support a belief system. One has only to think of the physical laws of Newton and his contemporaries, aimed at demonstrating 'the hand of God', and the theological contortions of pre-Darwinian geologists, to appreciate this point. Alchemy is another major example of a belief-led science.

If we try to define science as a disinterested, value-free quest for knowledge, aimed at understanding the nature of the physical world, we see that even now very little science, if any, satisfies this criterion. Most scientists answer to a paymaster and have to give lipservice, at least, to technological or social relevance in their work, and it is only in the most fundamental areas of basic research that true scientific endeavour has the opportunity to flourish. I myself can easily be tempted to fall into the 'golden age' trap by saying that the only true age of science was the Age of Reason in the eighteenth century, when natural philosophy was the pursuit of gentlemen of leisure! Although they had no funding body breathing down their necks for results and relevance, they did not have the technology to pursue their science in the way we do now. Those puzzled by the image of the eighteenth century

25. The mediaeval church at
Staunton-on-Arrow near Hereford
is built alongside a prehistoric moated
mound. This is a common feature on
the Welsh border and one that
prompted Alfred Watkins to include
such churches in his alignments.

26. A prominent mound on the Welsh
border is Turret Tump at Lower
Hengoed, near Hay-on-Wye. It
dominates the surrounding countryside, sitting atop the crest at the end
of a long ridge. Many alignments are
said to go through this striking
feature.

27. St Michael's Mount, Cornwall. This 'holy isle' with its crowning chapel is said to form the beginning of the St Michael's Line. Nevertheless, the occurrence of hilltop shrines and churches is often associated with the dragon-killing saint.

28. Geiger counter monitoring during Operation Merlin. In this case the author is assisted in using a scintillometer by Roy Cooper.
Photo : Paul Devereux

Opposite
29. The granite blocks of the Merry Maidens Circle near Penzance. The first negative Geiger anomaly was detected here: the level of Geiger activity was markedly lower than that outside.

30. The mysterious entrance to a Cornish fogou, used as one of the control sites for the Geiger monitoring at the Merry Maidens.

31. A granite outcrop or tor, used as a further control for the Geiger monitoring at the Merry Maidens.

32. Infrared photography at Rollright. The Kingstone in the weird light of dawn.
Photo : Paul Devereux

savant in the closing scenes of Kubrick's *2001* should, in fact, relish his unerring choice of this figure as the true scientist emerging from the technological cocoon before the 'rebirth'.

This golden age of pure science differed from our own in one major respect: observations of the natural world were limited by the range of the human senses. Even with microscopes and telescopes, existing senses were only slightly extended, and until the twentieth century this was how science progressed, dealing exclusively with the immediate world in an empirical way. The great majority of current hard sciences work well beyond the range of the human senses; perhaps the simplest example is the use of X-ray photography, using electromagnetic radiation that we cannot sense directly to provide information that we cannot obtain in the same way from our unaided sensory system. Likewise, most of our information at the molecular and atomic levels in the main areas of hard science—physics, chemistry, the earth and life sciences—employs energetics and sensors well outside our sensory range. These do not extend our senses in that they allow us directly to experience the phenomena being studied—these have to be represented in a way that our senses can respond to, and we see, for example, in infrared photography, that ordinary colours are used to express 'invisible colours' beyond the frequency range of our vision.

The hard sciences work at this deep level of reality within twentieth century frameworks while at the same time honouring the methods of scientific enquiry that are our legacy from the giants of the Renaissance and the Age of Reason. While the early researchers would be content to work empirically, however, and thus establish laws of nature that supported their religious beliefs, the objective of modern science is to press on into the deepest levels of reality accessible to our instruments; we are not content simply to label something and think that the label represents understanding. So much of what is called science consists of labelling—we call the attraction between bodies 'gravity' and can quantify the attraction without understanding it, in the same way as we define phototropism (turning towards light) in plants and territoriality in animals, without truly understanding the *real* reasons for their existence.

This descent to deep molecular, atomic and subatomic levels is denied the 'soft' sciences, those that are essentially descriptive and empirical. In many of these—particularly the favourite target, sociology—the phenomena are so complex and difficult to quantify that an empirical treatment may be the only feasible one; in the same spirit, some have defined biology as 'chemistry too difficult for chemists' and chemistry as 'physics too difficult for physicists': at certain levels one science fades into another as complexity or simplicity dictates. It is easy for non-scientists to miss this fact of merging

97

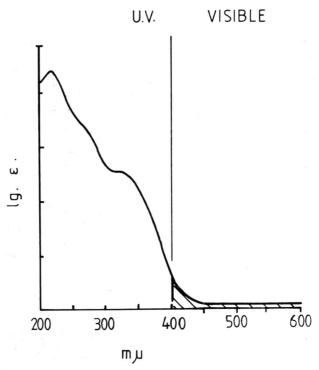

Fig 30. Seeing and Believing. Most visible colours are due to electronic excitations in the ultraviolet, and our eyes only perceive a minute fraction of this interaction. If we could imagine 'seeing' in the ultraviolet (as many insects do) the colours (which we cannot imagine!) would be hundreds of times more intense, and we would think the human visible region a pale and ghostly world. The shaded area in the graph is the tiny part of the spectrum of a 'coloured' substance we respond to! If the edge of the curve does not extend into the visible, we cannot 'see' the colour.

32. Direct interaction with the stones of Rollright: another aspect of the software programme, co-ordinated by John Steele, is the monitoring of psychics directly experiencing the Rollright atmosphere and ambience. Here John Steele looks on as trance-psychic John Gordon experiences the memory of the stones. (Photo: Paul Devereux)

99

and to castigate science for dealing in compartmentalisation at the expense of a holistic approach. For many decades, however, the classical divisions of science have ceased to have a meaningful existence and instead it is more realistic to visualise science as a nest of Chinese boxes with mathematics and physics at the centre, life sciences and earth sciences further out. All are interconnected, having higher and lower levels of complexity.

The technology demonstrated at the circles—geometrical, astronomical, constructional—neither requires a fundamental knowledge of the hidden levels of nature nor implies that such knowledge was generated by the exercise of circle construction. The science involved was empirical, however complex the geometry or sophisticated the astronomical alignments, and this is true whether we consider it technology or belief-led. In order to justify it, we do not need to invoke a parent high civilisation, whether in the past or elsewhere in the world, particularly when we place the circles in the mainstream of accelerating western technological advance.

This discussion does not denigrate the achievements of the megalith builders, it only seeks to show that simple answers or justifications for the circles can be made from our present state of knowledge. Equally, it tries to show that attempts to read modern science into the megaliths may be doomed to failure, because our knowledge of the fine structure of matter and energy was not approachable by this empirical route. We are, however, left with one awkward point: how do the ultrasonic anomalies square with this overall picture that seems to be consistent with a simple, empirical science?

This point will be explored more fully in the final chapters, but let me say here that it is not absolutely necessary to invoke modern scientific hardware for an awareness of this effect, or some by-product of it, to have existed in the megalith builders' minds. If, on the other hand, we suggest that the nature of ultrasound and methods for generating it were understood in our terms, then this implies a large supporting body of related knowledge of the physical world at the same level. Even if we suggest a strong, patient, empirical science wedded to either technology or belief, the question of ancient wisdom, and its shadow of ancient magic, has still not been addressed. Is there anything within the technology that expresses a wisdom beyond the empirical knowledge so far uncovered?

WISDOM BY NUMBERS

The search for an ancient wisdom has led many authors, notably John Michell and Geoffrey Ashe, to discuss the use of certain numbers by many ancient cultures to express knowledge or profound wisdom in a way that is only accessible to initiates of the system.

Such numerical systems undoubtedly existed in the past: one has only to think of the Kabala and the Book of Revelations with its constant numerical references, particularly to the 'number of the beast, 666', and the superstitious significance in the West of numbers such as 7 and 13, as immediate examples. The identification of sacred numbers, their linking to superstition—with its implication of a debased survival of ancient knowledge—and to initiates of secret knowledge, brings in many evocative aspects of ancient times: secret societies, the 'conspiracy theory' of history and the evidence for a shadowy grand design for humanity manipulated by such a secret society either located in a remote and inaccessible corner of the world or perhaps somewhere 'beyond'. Such a basis for an ancient wisdom has many irresistible ingredients for those wishing to find an underlying rationale for prehistory: if the system is universal, ancient and profound and has descended from a remote 'golden age' into the present through occult and secret routes involving alchemy, witchcraft, freemasonry and the ever-mysterious Knights Templars (who have been said to employ all three), then surely it must be associated with the megaliths, those landmarks of prehistory?

As with countless other connections that many would dearly love to trace back to megalithic times, the sheer lack of tangible evidence, while adding such an exciting aura of mystery to the whole question, distorts the picture since it can be so readily adapted to almost any theory of the ancient world. And so it is with the application of the whole apparatus of sacred numbers to the megaliths: it may be implausible but the very silence of the stones confers an air of irrefutability.

The numerology of the circles and of other major structures such as the Great Pyramid and the mediaeval cathedrals of Europe depends upon finding the numerical units of their geometry or structure and then linking that to sacred words or phrases.

The establishment of this relationship requires a consummate juggling act. The chosen language, the numerical values of the letters, the constitution of the key words or phrases, must be linked to the units of measurement of the structure involved. Since the objective is to demonstrate a universal proportion and harmony within one comprehensive system, certain recurrent numbers associated with a wide range of structures must be found. It might be argued that, with so many factors, some kind of concordance can be achieved by chance, and that the repetition of words or short phrases might be linked as convincingly to slogans or aphorisms as to sublime philosophical truths. Alternatively, the arrival at harmonious proportions in any kind of built structure, while quantifiable mathematically, is an essential aesthetic factor and may require no deeper level of justification.

It is not possible here to undertake a detailed survey or critique of the idea

101

α	β	y	δ	ε	ζ	η	Θ	ι	κ	λ	μ	ν
1	2	3	4	5	7	8	9	10	20	30	40	50

ξ	o	π	ρ	σ,ς	τ	υ	φ	χ	ψ	ω
60	70	80	100	200	300	400	500	600	700	800

Fig 31. The Science of Numbers. Gematria is said to ascribe numerical values to letters (here shown for the Greek alphabet) and expresses particular thoughts and relationships through numbers that represent sacred or significant words. The most famous number from Revelations (which is full of numerical references) is 666, the Number of the Beast or Antichrist.

of sacred numbers; but, if we accept Michell's contention that classical Greek, the fundamental units of alchemy and allusions to Christianity are all integral parts of the numerical system, whatever the harmony or beauty of the resulting concordances, it is difficult to see how they can be extended from mediaeval or classical times back to the circle builders. Similarly, Michell brings in all non-metric measurement systems—inch, foot, yard, megalithic yard, cubit and more—to arrive at the numbers, and centres almost everything upon the Great Pyramid.

This is given the number 1746, which is equated with the sum of the alchemic numbers for sulphur and mercury and with the classical Greek phrase 'grain of mustard seed', emphasising the Pyramid's numerical relationship with the dimensions of the earth. This subject, of course, is an intellectual quagmire, but in Michell's treatment Stonehenge is seen also to symbolise a whole range of sacred words or phrases, including Christian ones, by adroitly switching units and geometrical constructions.

One is left with an uneasy feeling that, by including so many places and names and measuring systems, and by using the classical Greek alphabet for structures such as the Great Pyramid and Stonehenge, a kind of spurious unity could be achieved—provided the net was cast wide enough in choosing structures and key phrases. It is not at all unlikely that there were arcane numerical systems of symbology amongst mediaeval cathedral builders and alchemists; whether these pointed to sublime truths, deep insights or misconceptions we cannot say, prevented by the sheer obscurity of the available information. The same problem arises when we appear to see early

102

Greek philosophers anticipating modern ideas of cosmology and stellar evolution—a famous factor in the 'Sirius Mystery' of Robert Temple. Untangling these nuggets of modern perceived wisdom from the voluminous and elliptical writings of the ancients may prompt us to give them more significance than they did: it could be a lucky guess, a flight of fancy, or it could be based on a detailed observation. We just do not know.

The links between mediaeval traditions and the beliefs and philosophies of the early farmers seem very tenuous indeed; while we may be seeing the celebration in stone of fundamentally satisfying proportions and ratios in construction, nothing else may be necessary to explain them, whatever labels and rationales may have been applied in a later age. Perhaps the wisdom so expressed amounts to no more than slogans or an intellectual blind alley. It does not get to the nub of the problem, does not rip the veil away from our own reality to expose its workings at a deeper level. The wisdom is still on the surface. Can we go below?

WISDOM AND REALITY

In the closing decades of the nineteenth century it was tempting to believe that the rise of science, accelerating ever since the Renaissance, had uncovered the fundamental truths of nature, and that the only endeavour left for scientists was the ever-increasing refinement of an essentially mechanistic model of the universe.

It is a matter of history, even legend, that, within the space of a few years, the discovery of radioactivity, the natural transmutation of elements, subatomic particles and the announcement of the theories of Relativity by Einstein, destroyed this cosy world view for ever. The 'New Physics'—a term we still use, although the major steps in its development were all taken more than half a century ago—ushered in a new world view from the deepest levels of matter and energy, showing that, in a seething cauldron of creation, they were different sides of an even more mysterious coin. The solid atoms of matter, created so lovingly from the speculations of the Greeks and the experiments of nineteenth century savants such as Dalton and Berzelius, vanished into a deeper picture of shifting forcefields and probability functions acting out a microcosmic drama on a vast and empty stage; for the overwhelming component of an atom was *nothing*—a vast yawning emptiness populated with brief lightning streaks of matter that seemed to have no physical existence.

This weird reality of matter at what appeared to be an ultimate level was summed up by the celebrated philosopher and physicist, Eddington, in the paradox of the 'two tables'. They occupied his study side-by-side: one solid

103

33. The vast, heavy sarsens of Avebury stand silently in the henge in the grey light of a winter afternoon. Whatever purpose we ascribe to the megalith builders, their skill and technological prowess command our respect and admiration.

104

and ordinary, subject to all the laws of the everyday empirical world; the other, a shifting, spinning phantasm of matter and energy that science told him was the real table. Yet were they the same table, or did he look at them in different ways and see two images that could not be reconciled because he used a different conceptual system to accommodate each?

A yawning gulf suddenly appeared between the empirical world, the world of direct observation, of 'common sense', and the microscopic world. The empirical world contained the microscopic world many times over, but with the 'strangeness' cancelled out by the sheer weight of numbers of all the particles. The microscopic world obeyed its own laws in a vastly different setting and could not be comprehended, let alone explained, in terms of the everyday world.

The bizarre nature of this world under our feet, this seemingly ultimate reality, was itself dissected by the rise of high energy physics: the nuclear building blocks, protons and neutrons, were themselves seen to consist of an almost infinite perspective of smaller entities. These were revealed by using higher and higher impact energies to split nuclear particles into smaller and smaller fragments.

Even the shadowy substance of the atomic world established by the early twentieth century physicists gradually began to fade like the Cheshire Cat, leaving a phantom grin across the face of particle physics: the particles that came out balanced the energy that went in. We seemed to be interacting with the particles we were observing, and to be looking down an abyss of creation that had no end amongst the infinitely small particles where they emerged from an energy net. Matter was frozen energy; but what was energy?

This insubstantial, ghostly world of the ultimate seemed to many physicists to exist almost as a philosophical abstraction, and there were some who found striking parallels with the teachings of the mystical religions of the Orient. It seemed that, millennia before, the merging of space, time and energy found by our most advanced and fundamental sciences had been anticipated by eastern sages. Furthermore, the Buddhist belief that the reality we perceive is an illusion, albeit an extremely convincing one, struck a sympathetic chord among philosophically inclined physicists; they began to feel that the results of their work, employing the highest technology and finest minds of western science, had all been anticipated by the ancient sages. Truly, here was an ancient wisdom worthy of the name: profound insights into the ultimate nature of the physical world gained through a deep belief system almost completely alien to western thought! Those who saw a global high civilisation in the past, underpinning all the achievements of antiquity, at last found their justification: the wisdom existed in the East, a fundamental

105

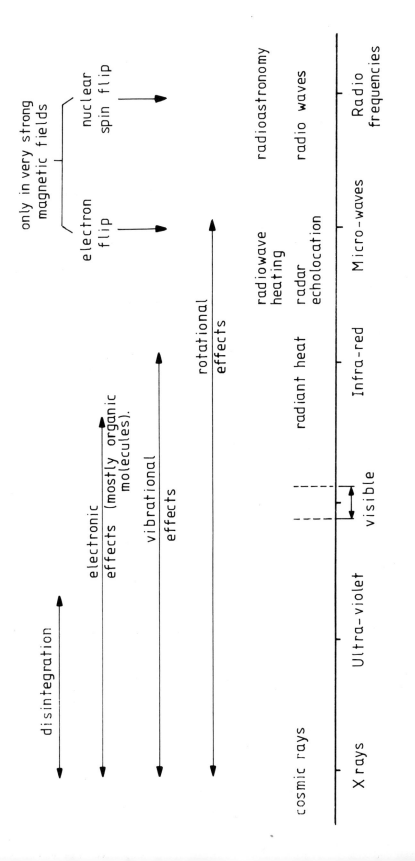

Fig 32. Matter and Energy. Electromagnetism interacts with matter at all levels of energy. Free electrons respond to very weak energies by 'spin flipping' and to stronger ultraviolet energies by 'orbital hopping' or excitation which invariably leads to colour. Higher energy interactions always involve *every* stage of the lower energy interactions so that, as the energy increases, molecules or atoms are progressively torn apart.

science existed as a religion, and in the past it could have released untold powers to its initiates.

However profound the Buddhist, Taoist or Hindu concepts of the nature of reality, and however ecstatic the reaction of the physicists to the startling concordances, it comes as something of a shock to realise that the concepts of ceaseless change and decay, of the 'stillness' of a dynamic equilibrium where a 'mental snapshot' gives the illusion of absence of movement, have a firm basis in the macroscopic, everyday world. Brownian movement in liquids, our perception of sensory paradoxes or illusions and the inwardly perceived non-linear nature of time can all provide, from everyday experience, the basis for profound insights into the workings of the natural world, without anticipating the present-day knowledge of particle physics and its philosophical abstractions.

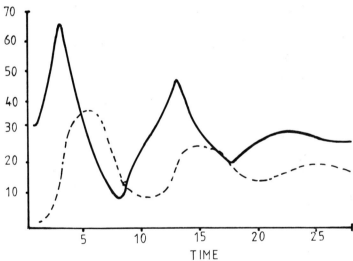

Fig 33. Dynamic Equilibrium in the Everyday World. Interactions of two populations—the dotted line is the predator; the solid line is the prey. Each population has an impact on the other, which tends to keep a dynamic equilibrium. Such an equilibrium could well have been noted and even understood in the remote past.

107

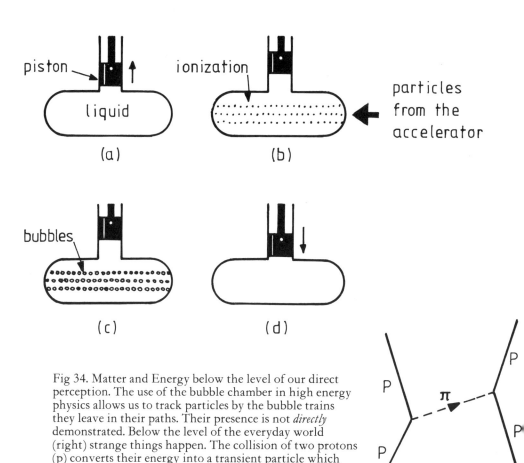

Fig 34. Matter and Energy below the level of our direct perception. The use of the bubble chamber in high energy physics allows us to track particles by the bubble trains they leave in their paths. Their presence is not *directly* demonstrated. Below the level of the everyday world (right) strange things happen. The collision of two protons (p) converts their energy into a transient particle which only exists in the brief interval of collision.

We can read in many books dealing with ancient sciences how the weird properties and behaviour of subatomic particles explain many of the mysteries of those sciences and show how the ancients manipulated with contemptuous ease natural forces that we can now only unlock with vast high energy machines. It has even been suggested that the 'world-lines' of anti-particles created in collisions can explain the strange behaviour of UFOs!

Certainly the philosophical paradoxes and sheer strangeness of these ultimate particles invite their invocation to explain bizarre phenomena and deep insights into nature. But what is forgotten is that the 'buying-in' price to this world is astronomically high in energy terms and that the weird phenomena are not exhibited in the energetics of the everyday world. They

108

are locked far, far below the realm of our ordinary lives, and who can say that any of these phenomena can be predicted *in isolation*, with no information at all to lean on? Who might, for example, predict without a basis that the sky is blue or a candle flame is yellow?

However tempting the correspondence of the new physics and ancient mysticism, we still cannot really justify stepping beyond the everyday empirical realm to give scientific reality to these religious insights. What we must invoke in any identification of a past empirical ancient science is a way beyond introspection and contemplation to an interaction with the forces that are predicted.

Such an interaction has been suggested and the instrument would have been accessible to any one in ancient times. It is *ourselves*, our reaction to these mysterious forces behind the megaliths. Need we look further than obeying the injunction, 'the proper study of mankind is man'?

7
UNDERSTANDING
THE EARTH

Not knowing that one knows is best.
Lao Tzu

The science and technology of the circles is impressive in its scope and sophistication, although there is little to show that the science reached beyond an empirical level. Perhaps the way through to a deeper understanding of nature, implied by the discovery of the energy anomalies, falls outside such science as we see and experience directly?

LOOKING AND SEEING

We can look at the circles in many different ways, and it is a deeply human trait to perceive what one is looking for and what one expects to find, rather than what is there. In the work at Rollright described in this book these preconceptions were swept away as far as possible; the discovery of energy anomalies cut through the Gordian knot of research on the circles by generating a wholly unexpected body of data which did not really fit any of the conventional scenarios, orthodox or unorthodox. As we shall see in the concluding chapter, this devastating effect has only been heightened by the unexpected discovery of Geiger counter anomalies.

The science and technology of the circles, so patiently uncovered by Hawkins and Thom, still stand, depending upon their acceptance, at a zenith of megalithic achievement. They represent, nevertheless, an empirical approach, and we have to see how the anomalies uncovered by the Dragon Project can either be accommodated within that empiricism, or whether they fall outside. Since we are dealing, in both cases, with phenomena which occur beyond the accepted range of our unaided sensory systems, we are left with some uncomfortable choices. If we suggest that the megalith builders had a *scientific* awareness of these phenomena (in our modern sense of the word), then we have to insist that such an awareness could only have existed within a much larger scientific framework. To appreciate the need for this infrastructure, you have only to consider what information, facts and

110

equipment you need to answer the question, 'what is an electron?'

Our overall picture of neolithic gross empirical science gives no evidence of such a scientific sophistication. Indeed, to speak of science in this way is probably misleading, since what we think of as their science was probably indistinguishable from religion and magic. After all, is not magic a science or technology we do not understand? And if we do not understand something which is marvellous, does this not lead down the road to religion?

Whether the energy anomalies were due to site, stones or a combination of the two factors is not, at this point, important. What matters is the *perception* of the anomaly. If a science and technology of anticipation and detection did not exist, then we are left with the suggestion that the manifestation of the anomaly was *directly* perceived; whatever its source, it seems likely that it was a fundamental feature of location, structure or both. The implications of this line of elimination are quite stunning: if we deny a direct sensory access to such phenomena, we are left with the interpretation of subtle environmental clues related to the discovered anomalies (these, of course, may be minor features of other more fundamental anomalies, but we cannot pronounce on them at this stage!), and here we come back to the overall empiricism of the construction of the circles. Perhaps there was a wisdom underpinning the obvious features of megalithic science that saw through to the more fundamental, subtle aspects of nature, possibly without what we would call a 'scientific understanding' of what was perceived, but rather with a recognition of 'something' that was deemed of overwhelming significance.

There is a yawning divide between 'looking' and 'seeing', a distinction drawn in many philosophies, in many different ways, to signify penetrating through the obvious, superficial cloak of the material world to an inner reality. Such an insight, in this context, conflicts neither with the overall empiricism nor with the archaeological perspective. We are dealing here with human qualities and feelings, moving onto the dark stage of hunches and intuitions, feelings of 'rightness' and the like. Yet, even in science, we ignore this at our peril, since it often provides the inspiration that gives substance to most scientific endeavours. Can we put our finger on these anomalies and perceive them unaided by instruments—is this the key to the overall mystery of the circles? Many people have been insisting for years that this can be done and was done by the megalith builders. The study of the 'human factor' in the circles is fiercely controversial, one that as a physical scientist I try to avoid, but we cannot ignore this dimension since, after all, archaeology is about how people lived. This may be the nettle that we have to grasp to understand the central mystery of the circles and their builders.

111

DIVINING THE EARTH

The starting point of the Dragon Project was the confused and enormous mass of legend, folklore and anecdote that spoke of some kind of energy associated with stone circles, an energy known and utilised by the megalith builders. One strange body of evidence tells of how this energy can still be recognised today, and recognised directly in a way that the ancients could have perceived it; this evidence is open to anyone who wishes to explore it.

We are talking, of course, of dowsing or divining. There is no space in this book to go into the scientific debate over the reality, or otherwise, of dowsing. It is one of the 'human interaction' aspects of the Dragon Project which will be described by others in due course in relation to the overall Project.

What is dowsing? There are many definitions, but let us say, deceptively simply, that it is a facility to respond to hidden objects or forces with the aid, for example, of a forked rod or pendulum. In some cases this response occurs unaided. It is most commonly encountered in the context of water divining where certain individuals routinely locate water and indicate the exact spot and depth to drill in an otherwise barren landscape.

I came across dowsing when my interest in stone circles was being aroused. What does a prosaic physical scientist make of dowsing? The immediate reaction is to dismiss it out of hand, thinking that there must be a simple explanation, but the next and obvious step is to try it. This I did with a buried water main, using a forked twig, and, to my amazement and even alarm, I underwent the 'dowsing reaction'; the twig forced itself up, twisting out of my grip so that it required considerable force to prevent it moving, leaving me with aching forearms as a memento! I had similarly disconcerting reactions in other contexts using a pendulum, where the reaction manifests itself as a strong rotation suddenly starting up in a motionless hand-held pendulum.

As with all such 'paranormal' phenomena (although if they really exist they should rather be described as unusual), it is easy to be tempted into the 'parlour-trick' syndrome, although my consternation at being faced with an apparently inexplicable phenomenon was not easy to live with at first. It is, however, an arrogance of science, and many scientists, to think that everything can be explained and that those things that cannot be explained, by falling outside science, do not really exist. We might recall here the story of Eddington's 'two tables' and add to it a third, one where we appreciate

34. Two faces of the Dragon: electronics engineer Rodney Hale monitors one of the Kingsmen for ultrasonic emanations, while the eminent dowser Bill Lewis looks on with interest. (Photo: Paul Devereux)

112

113

the grain, colour, style and proportions of the table, irrespective of its scientific attributes. Because emotional and aesthetic responses cannot at present be fully explained, it does not mean that they do not exist, and it is the responsibility of any scientist to try to place his or her work into this wider 'human' context.

I uncovered a wide and comprehensive literature of dowsing responses at stone circles and menhirs, and at ancient sites in general. That there was some kind of activity, in abundance, seemed beyond doubt from the enthusiastic accounts of the devotees and 'initiates', and it was something I was to experience personally many times, alone and under their guidance, at these sites. The literature of dowsing is an arcane one where subjective responses to the phenomenon are inextricably bound up both with quasi-scientific theorising and conjecture and discussions about *what* is being detected. In any scientific endeavour it requires long experience and a certain boldness simply to observe and record. I always liken this to the military dictum about holding fire 'until you see the whites of their eyes'! One might observe, however, that there is no reason why dowsing should follow scientific criteria, and possibly even less reason to try to mix science into something which is uniquely experiential.

So what do the dowsers find? They detect patterns of 'energy'—spirals, rings, lines—all around these sites and around many others, ranging throughout all history and prehistory. This 'energy' is often related by them to the presence of underground water, and while there is little argument about dowsers successfully finding underground water, there is no record, so far as I am aware, of anyone drilling to find these evocatively-named 'blind springs' underneath stone circles. Some dowsers detect lines of energy coming from stone circles and running at different heights above the ground to other ancient sites, and have speculated on whether this forms the underpinning of the ley concept.

Whether it is water or energy, something untoward seems connected with these sites and may point to their identification and marking with stone in ancient times. It is only a short step from this to say that the ancients— whether astronomer priests, diviners, magicians or something else—were in close touch with the earth and could instinctively sense these anomalous places. And who can deny this possibility outright? Most of us would agree that certain places have an 'atmosphere'—we respond to it, finding some places welcoming, others friendly, sad or even frightening. Whether this is due to the place itself or to events that occurred there, or whether the place 'triggered' the events, we may not be able to say, and in the same way we may not be able to quantify this atmosphere (although there have been attempts to understand how it might arise), but this does not deny its

114

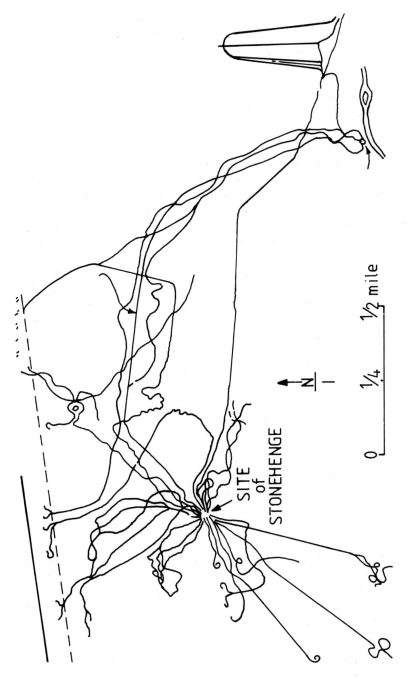

Fig 35. Dowsing. Convergence of 'water-lines' on the site of Stonehenge. The dense packing of some lines in the Stonehenge car park has led some dowsers to suggest that it is due more to usage by people leaving detectable traces than to the site itself!

115

existence. Everyone can probably think of responses to 'atmosphere': in my own case I find Stonehenge oppressive, Avebury benign and I have never 'felt' anything either way at Rollright; and one could go on to discuss other, non-megalithic, sites that have made a deep impression from their atmosphere.

Some dowsers, notably Tom Graves, have reflected that perhaps they are indeed picking up traces of events, which implies a 'recording' capability in the immediate environment, itself possibly a function of the anomaly. Outlandish as this suggestion seems, I witnessed a demonstration of a dowsing phenomenon even more bizarre that may be relevant: it is said to be possible to *think* a straight line so that someone can get a dowsing response when he or she crosses it. I saw this happen, and it happened to me as well, under controlled conditions!

Phenomena such as this show that, whatever one may think of the theorising and explanations, it is unwise to dismiss the dowsing response. It may well hold the key to the ancient identification of the sites in terms of an unquantified and uncomprehended anomaly outside the framework of demonstrable megalithic science. It does not argue for a deep, quantitative understanding of nature but for a keen, developed awareness and empathy with the environment; so say the exponents of the dowsing approach, and they may well be right.

But what *are* they responding to? Many things have been suggested, magnetism being one of the favourites, although the continual variation of the earth's magnetic field with time may not make this a very strong contender, particularly where water is concerned. It is difficult to see how they could be responding to the *detected* anomalies at Rollright. Experiments to determine the energy to which dowsing adepts respond give levels that are so minute they almost defy belief. We stand, then, looking down into a bottomless abyss: is there really something down there, something that once held the key, something that most of us have since lost? Are the mystics right?

LINES OF FORCE

The ley concept—that prehistoric sites are aligned—is a very potent one. On the one hand, it is welcomed by those mystically inclined because it supports the argument for a vanished civilisation living in harmony with the earth and moulding it to enhance its beneficial influences. This is a quintessentially 'golden age' rhapsody, with the implication that the alignment of sacred sites had an energetic function, directing a mysterious force beneficially over wide landscapes. The unnatural straightness has also

35. Arbor Low: this enigmatic site, with its large embankment and curiously flattened stone circle, has been invoked at various times as the focus of a vast network of aligned ancient sites. (Photo: Duncan MacNeil)

been discussed in terms of *removing* a malevolent force from the landscape. It becomes entwined both with numerology and gematria where mystic proportions arc said to enhance such energies, and with divining in the broadest sense, where it is called geomancy; the evidence of the existing Chinese practice of *Feng-shui* is used to support this contention.

Whether there is anything in this idea, other than the desire for a golden age allied to an appreciation of harmony in proportion, is difficult to say. On the other hand, orthodox archaeology is generally hostile to the idea, and this pronounced lack of enthusiasm extends both to the often questionable choice of sites for the alignment markers (these often include old churches, market crosses and crossroads, in the belief that they are recent accretions on the sites of lost ancient markers) and to the impossibility of visualising lengthy alignments across a Britain that was probably heavily forested at

117

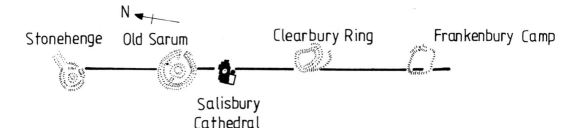

Fig 36. Ley or Nay? The Stonehenge-Clearbury Ring alignment has taxed many a telephoto lens in the quest for intervisibility, and on a map we can see that the immediate alignment looks impressive. But how do we reconcile the wide date-range of the sites and the dense concentration of other ancient sites in the area to the choice of this mixture of sites, ranging from neolithic circle to Iron Age camp and mediaeval cathedral? Perhaps it is the *hint* of ancient order that is more impressive than any statistical argument for or against.

that stage in the neolithic era. Others point out that some of the evocatively named 'grand' alignments—for example the St. Michael's Line from Cornwall to Lowestoft that takes in Stonehenge, Glastonbury and a host of other sites often associated with the dragon-killing archangel, St. Michael—are only straight on a planar map projection. Transferred to a normal curved surface, they are wildly out.

Possibly the truth lies somewhere in between. Acceptance of the broad archeo-astronomical picture due to Thom implies that some alignments do exist, and recent statistical work has suggested that the alignment of some sites over short distances (ideally three or four miles) is too significant to be mere chance. Statisticians, of course, have a field day in this dispute: with so many ancient sites in Britain, chance alignments of a very convincing character can emerge from any Ordnance Survey map. The opportunity for self-deception in drawing lines on maps is enormous, and many alignments break down when subjected to even minor statistical treatment. This does not mean to say, however, that the statistical 'demonstration' of an alignment actually means anything in archaeological terms or does more than give a point for departure in any discussion of 'earth energy'.

Fig 37. Most dramatic of the proposed alignments in Britain are the Sunrise (or St Michael's) Line and the Belinus Line, which intersect at Avebury. Impressive as they look on a conventional Mercator projection map, their placing on a realistic *curved* surface creates havoc with the concept! Map alignments over some tens of miles are seriously affected by the earth's curvature (see overleaf).

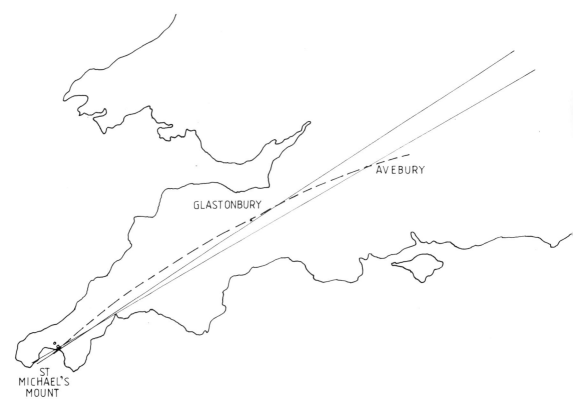

ST
MICHAEL'S
MOUNT

GLASTONBURY

AVEBURY

Fig 38. The curved dotted line is the Sunrise Line allowing for curvature. If it goes through Glastonbury and Avebury it will not continue the line to the east coast.

Fig 39. Points on a Landscape. The Hereford-Powys borderland is a rich repository of ancient sites and this was the area that gave birth to Watkins' ley concept. If we look at the early mediaeval churches and barrows scattered for several miles around the Whetstone on Hergest Ridge (25 miles west of Hereford), can we see real alignments, or are they a consequence of what has survived through three and half thousand years? Again, there is the tantalising hint of order.

120

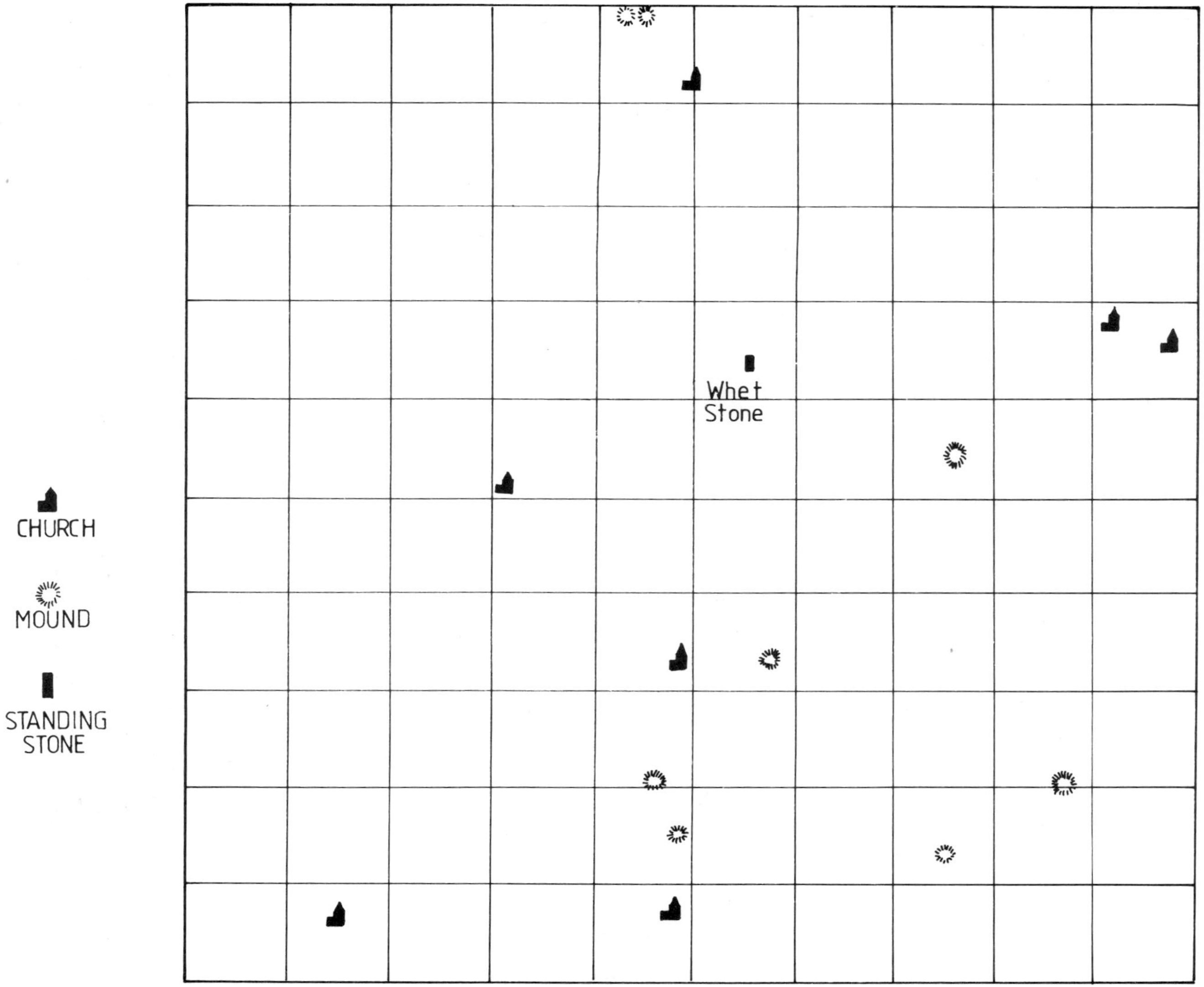

Whet
Stone

CHURCH

MOUND

STANDING
STONE

And yet, if these sites are the foci of energy anomalies, however these fit into our scientific picture of energy in the earth, how do these square with their occurrence in straight lines? It is often said that nature abhors a straight line, but the unlikelihood of a straight alignment marking the transmission of any mysterious force through the earth is countered on two fronts: one, that the force may not actually be in the ground, the other, that the *manipulation* into straight lines is the real key; although there is a disquieting overtone here, drawn from *Feng Shui*, that such manipulation of meandering, sinuous energy is an undesirable activity.

In rehearsing these arguments the reader may indeed sympathise with my desire simply to take measurements and stay outside the war of words! However, even if ignored, these ideas will not just go away, and the work at Rollright certainly provides a basis for assessing them afresh.

36. & 37. The evolution of ancient sites. Many prehistoric sites are associated with mediaeval churches, even when such siting divorces the church from its attendant village. A famous example is Breedon-on-the-Hill in Leicestershire, where the church is located on top of a prominent hill fort with the village left below (36). Less well known is the mediaeval church at Great Wolford (37), a few miles from Rollright, which is built within the ramparts of a prehistoric earthworks with the village ranged closely alongside. (Photo No. 36: Duncan MacNeil)

8
THE DRAGON'S LAIR

The rest is silence.
William Shakespeare,
Hamlet, Prince of Denmark,
v. 2

The evidence of folklore, the studies of ancient science and human interaction at ancient sites depend ultimately upon subjective evidence which can be argued over endlessly. The work of the Dragon Project has pointed to a way forward from this speculative circle, forward into a silent world beyond our immediate senses, beyond squabbling over interpretations of legend and hearsay.

FIVE MINUTE WONDER

Casual tourists and local inhabitants had all taken note, in their various ways, of the measuring sessions at Rollright, and soon the inevitable happened and we came to the attention of the media. The interest, when it came, posed a dilemma for many Project members. Obviously, any publicity was worth having if it helped us to raise funds to continue the work, and we had little doubt that the whole thrust of the Project, and its startling results, were both newsworthy and of scientific interest across a wide front. The problem posed was more fundamental: would it be trivialised, sensationalised or otherwise presented at the 'parlour trick' level?

From my own point of view this was a vital consideration. In the autumn of 1979, I had been given a year's Research Fellowship at the Institute of Archaeology in London University. I was beginning to get somewhere with the strange world of trapped electrons, showing how they could give archaeological information. I had been given a year's leave from teaching and the prospect of entering the orthodox world of archaeological science full-time was beginning to seem more than a dream. Would the publicising of Rollright affect this? Yet my evolving background as an orthodox researcher was one of the strongest cards to play since, if I could deliver on that front, then it implied I might do the same thing at Rollright.

The deciding factor was really the possibility that, if we did not report it or have some hand in the method of reporting this most unusual work, others would do it instead at second hand, and that was something to avoid at all costs if we wanted to present the story as prosaically and factually as possible.

The chance for a sympathetic presentation emerged in the summer of 1979, in the magazine *Alpha*. Although I was able to give a bald, unemotional and fairly lengthy account of the project findings, the general paranormal context of the magazine was more than a little worrying. Although the paranormal connotations were obvious and exciting, I was at pains to stress that we wanted to get away from any connection with the paranormal where so much of the discussion seems to dwell on the veracity of witnesses and phenomena and the possibility of fraud. All I wanted to do was present the data, so that any interested and competent scientist could go into the field and repeat it. In other words, I hoped to raise the level of the debate and shake off the 'loonies in a field' image of earth energy hunting.

The response was more than encouraging. *Alpha* launched the magazine issue, with our article leading, at a press conference on a boiling hot day in a City of London pub. The response was enthusiastic, and led immediately to a string of radio interviews and press pieces; our contact with the BBC World Service, where the science staffers were sympathetic and positive, was extremely encouraging.

But what could we do for an encore? We had shot our proverbial bolt, made our interim statement and now looked ahead to a long period of back-up work. But journalists have their own priorities and, since we were unwilling to speculate on the meaning of our findings, interest flagged after a while. None of this activity, overwhelming as it seemed at the time, made any discernible impact in the wider world. The occasional brush with interested scientists and archaeologists did not evoke a hostile reaction. Our insistence on the need for further work, by us and other interested parties, more or less disarmed those who might be inclined to scoff. Several public lectures met with approval, except perhaps from die-hard mystics who felt that the science was antipathetic to their views.

It seemed the subject *could* be discussed. We had moved slightly away from the lunatic fringe, and into the second year of the Project. This *did* prove, in the Spring of 1980, to be the encore!

ENTER MERLIN

The idea of moving away from isolated monitoring runs at Rollright began to emerge during 1979 and, towards the end of the year, Paul Devereux managed to draw all the logistical threads together to ensure a virtually round-the-clock monitoring session from mid-February to mid-March, 1980. After the terrible winter of 1979, we hoped this coming one would be milder, for the February–March period was the obvious one to try, following the spectacular results the previous year. Hardy volunteers were mustered, monitoring timetables were arranged, heating, food supplies, spare batteries, extra detectors—all had to be taken to the little hut on the Rollright site. John Steele, the archaeologist responsible for the 'human interaction' side, arranged a schedule of dowsers and psychics so that they could play their part and see whether our instrumental responses tied in with their subjective ones. He also coined the name for the operation—Merlin, or OM1 as it became to us.

OM1 was a unique experience for all concerned, with the nomadic existence and the unexpected face of the countryside seen for prolonged periods at that time of the year. Overall, the weather held and the monitors braved the inevitable problems and privations. I travelled out from London regularly to see what was going on, how the equipment and the monitors were coping and how the results were shaping up. The local press, radio and even police took a sporadic interest, looking in from time to time, and the energy monitoring became something of a tourist attraction in itself. The schedule was arduous and exacting, although it was one I had worked out and tried myself before asking anyone to follow it. It was based on a generous selection of points around the immediate site, with control sites further afield, stretching to about a one-mile radius of the circle. The schedule did not allow much time for rest, as it involved repeating a four-hour circuit four times a day and several times at night, depending on the weather.

The schedule included both the established ultrasonic and Geiger counter monitoring, together with a range of additional features such as soil resistivity recording, a technique routinely employed in archaeology to detect buried structures, and electrical measurements of dowsing responses. So much data was produced during OM1 that the analysis is still continuing and the magnitude of the task has been compounded by data produced during subsequent OM sessions.

The highlight of OM1 was, naturally, the unexpected results, and these included the discovery of a Geiger counter anomaly. The basic monitoring pattern around the site involved certain fixed points at which ultrasonic and Geiger readings were taken, and several of these positions were located in the roadway between the circle and Kingstone.

During the first week, ultrasonic pulsings were detected around the circle and Kingstone at intensities and durations comparable to the previous year, but the Geiger readings showed nothing beyond the range to which we had

126

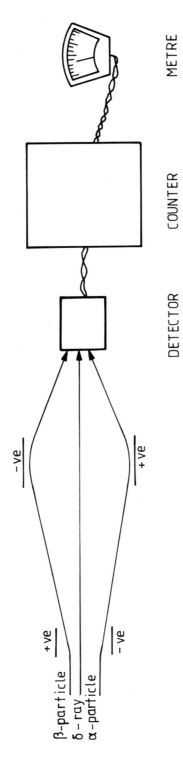

Fig 40. A Simple Geiger Counter. It responds to incoming radiation (which can be discriminated by electrical charge) and measures the level in counts per minute (cpm) through a meter reading and/or an audible output.

127

grown accustomed. In the second week, however, John Merron, who had moved into the hut for the week, decided to take extra readings in the roadway, and it was on the edge of the road by the circle that the anomaly was found. It was a 'hot spot', with readings several times greater than our background average. This 'hot spot' lay *between* the circle and Kingstone.

Geiger counter readings are always averages because they deal with an essentially random event. The rate of radioactive decay follows well-defined laws and involves the three characteristic particles, alpha, beta and gamma; but each individual disintegration, which is recorded by the counter, can occur at any time; it is the *overall* rate which averages out these events, very much as actuarial tables in a life insurance company give average life expectancies upon which insurance premiums are based (although these tables cannot predict when any *one* individual will die).

Geiger counter readings taken in the open air measure not only alpha, beta and gamma from the surroundings, but also the mysterious cosmic rays which streak through the earth's atmosphere from outer space. With our counter we measured the total counts over three or five minute periods to arrive at counts per minute (cpm) as our basic unit. Overall, the background in the surrounding countryside and at the circle was about 21 cpm, with an 'average' spread from 15–30 cpm. This was similar to values we obtained in London, Oxford and many control sites within several miles of Rollright. Compared with sophisticated counters our machine was primitive, but even so the consistency of results and the robustness and ease of handling made it an ideal machine for the initial Project work.

The readings alongside the verge between the circle and Kingstone were around 60–80 cpm, considerably higher than the background. They were very localised—in a strip about $1\frac{1}{2}$–2 feet wide and 12–15 feet long along the verge, and quite consistently high. Many subsequent determinations with other machines, some of the same type, others of much more sophisticated design, gave a comparable difference between the hot-spot and the background. (In simple terms, the more sensitive the counter, the greater number of events it will respond to, therefore giving higher count rates in any particular situation. It is the *relative* differences in individual machine count rates that are comparable.)

We were immediately elated, then puzzled, but soon afterwards we began to look for an obvious explanation. One possibility that immediately came to mind was the gravel in the road surface. Suppose there was a small section with higher than average radiation levels? But was it likely that such a small local sample could occur?

The road complicated matters, and ideally we should have preferred a site without one running through it. The Project went on, however, and after

38. Monitoring the Kingstone at dawn. Rodney Hale testing an electrostatic detector of his own devising as part of the physical monitoring programme of the Dragon Project. (Photo: Paul Devereux)

OM1 we noticed that, while the 'hot-spot' always had a level above the upper range of the background, it was sometimes in the 40–60 cpm region, at other times 60–80 cpm. This variation seem to argue against the road surface causing the effect, since if it were doing so it should remain relatively steady. Examination of the surface material away from the site further confirmed that it was not interfering with the readings.

The proponents of underground streams at stone circles immediately fixed upon the cause of the variation as the ebb and flow of radioactive traces being carried below the surface by underground water. But was it plausible for this effect to be transmitted through underlying rock and soil to a hand-held detector?

We just did not know. We had an anomaly, but it was nowhere near as clear-cut as the dramatic ultrasonic pulsing, and it was hedged by concern over spurious sources. To add to our confusion, collation of all the Geiger data, adding up to many thousands of readings, indicated something that we had suspected for some time: the readings around the Kingstone seemed slightly lower than the rest of the site. The difference, however, was very slight, one that would require more sophisticated counting and a statistical analysis. What we really needed now was a site where some of these effects, if they were real, would be more pronounced. This meant finding other sites to carry out pilot Geiger counter work. The Project was starting, therefore, to move its base.

Merlin had spoken. Yet again the ultrasound anomaly had been found, but the Geiger anomaly, although interesting, was tantalisingly vague. It seemed that *something* was there. What it all meant in terms of the overall site anomaly was a question to defer until we had some more definite evidence.

THE FOURTH EXPERIMENT

After OM1 the Project team was in a dilemma. Financially, we had shot our bolt; the funds available—generated by personal donations, mainly from readers of *The Ley Hunter* who had responded to an appeal from the editor, Paul Devereux—had all been used up on instrumentation and support for this unique effort. What were we to do next?

Fig 41. Nature Strikes Back. How the Fourth Experiment provides a pitfall for the unwary (and the wary!). Nevertheless, it leads into the uncharted territory of the fifth experiment...

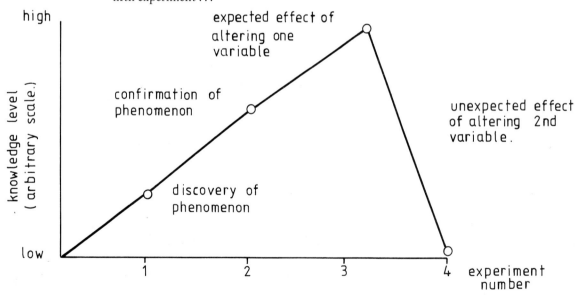

There were two conflicting priorities. On the one hand, we needed to carry out much more detailed work on both phenomena at Rollright, upgrading our machinery considerably; on the other, the Geiger results made measurements at another site imperative.

We managed to limp through 1980 doing a little bit of both, in a spirit of compromise, and to eke out Project resources. Rodney Hale, an internationally respected electronics engineer, began the construction of an upgraded ultrasonic detector and, using his own devices, secured for us the first verification of our ultrasonic results. Roy Cooper negotiated the loan of a very sensitive radiation counter and carried out independent readings at Rollright which confirmed our original findings and gave details on the components of the measured radioactivity. It was this kind of verification that we wanted and needed, but still the real demand was for an extensive programme of work that went far beyond our pilot efforts.

The demands of earning a living were also having their effect upon the Project. A successful application to the Threshold Foundation had provided sufficient funds for Paul Devereux to relinquish some of his teaching to devote more time to organisation and data collation. During 1980, the scope for my own research in orthodox archaeological science broadened and, with the prospect of a return to my previous teaching in the Autumn of 1980, a drive to avoid it by establishing myself in orthodox archaeology began and inevitably exacted a toll on my commitment to the Project.

Nevertheless, a trickle of funding continued to flow into the Project during 1980 and results were produced. I eventually returned to teaching, suffering an enormous culture shock after my year's leave of absence, and Paul Devereux moved to Wales as part of his reorganisation to cope with the Project data and his own writing career. The forward thrust of the Project seemed to be slipping from our grasp at the moment when a big effort was needed, and it was at this most unpromising time that two major events occurred.

The first one had enormous personal significance and also affected the Project in a crucial way. Almost resigning myself to a continued career in teaching, a chance of applying for a long-term Research Fellowship at the Institute presented itself out of the blue. I applied and against all the odds received it. That meant returning to academe for a further five years from October 1981, and my current return to teaching was therefore only temporary. Since my Fellowship carried faculty status and would involve international collaboration in archaeology, it meant that I was, in effect, the Project's 'mole' among the academics. I could actually speak from the inside, but more importantly, the increasing tide of publications arising from my orthodox work, including features in *Nature* and more recently *Science*, meant

131

that the 'knock-on' effect from my orthodox methods and strategies to the Project would begin to carry some weight. Overall, I had suddenly emerged from the Project back room to be its spokesman, coming out to present and defend the Project on academic ground. The importance of this development was incalculable, although the worry remained, at the back of my mind, as to how my superiors would view any publicity that we might generate on a larger scale!

This welcome but unexpected development was paralleled by the results from an experiment I had suggested to Paul Devereux which now became possible to execute. For some time I had been reflecting on the Geiger anomaly, its veracity (which now seemed demonstrated by a variety of independent checks), and how we might pursue it at other sites.

It occurred to me, one day, that perhaps a useful control experiment would be to measure Geiger activity at circles in a high-background area. Would we see the activity correspondingly enhanced, or would there be some different behaviour? The obvious choices of location were Cornwall and North-East Scotland, both areas of granite with relatively high radioactive levels from this mineral, and both areas with extensive concentrations of stone circles. Our choice narrowed to Cornwall since one of our monitors, Alan Bleakley, lived in Penzance and was familiar with the Geiger procedure. It was arranged, during 1981, to send him the Geiger counter with an experimental plan.

This I constructed quickly since, working in the dark, it was difficult to plan too far ahead. I suggested that several circles should be measured both inside and outside for varying distances around, and that readings should also be taken where the underlying granite was exposed, at cliff-faces in caves and at granite tors, for example, where the presence of large amounts of rock might give high readings from a 'mass effect'. Another control was to measure inside the strange Cornish subterranean passages, or fogous, where the enclosed space would give higher than expected readings due to the trapping of radon gas.

So what did I expect to find? A higher background level, a level higher than that at cliff-faces and in the fogous to give some comparison with a circle hot spot? Certainly, as far as the plan went, and working at several

39. & 40. The Fourth Experiment in Cornwall. Further tests on sites with high radioactive backgrounds led the Dragon Project to the Land's End peninsula which has many megalithic remains. The high background level due to granitic rocks was found to be dramatically reduced inside stone circles, the first one being the Merry Maidens (39), although levels in the proximity of granite masses, such as the interior of this stone-lined fogou (40), were found to be at an expectedly high level.

132

removes, the most I hoped for was a 'toe in the water' to give a clue for the next, more organised, experiment. This brings us to the 'Fourth Experiment' syndrome.

It has been observed by a number of researchers that one's efforts are often confounded by the 'Fourth Experiment'. The first experiment identifies a phenomenon, and the second confirms it. The third experiment varies a parameter, confirming the phenomenon further, but the fourth experiment varies another parameter—and produces a totally unexpected result! Put another way, the cosy growth of knowledge we anticipated is neatly side-stepped by nature whom I respect more and more as I become increasingly involved in research, and who shows that one really understands nothing!

The readings at the Cornish circles—several in the vicinity of Penzance were measured—were classic Fourth Experiment material. The background near the circles averaged 40 cpm (30–55 cpm), higher than at Rollright and certainly around the order anticipated. Levels near rockface and in the fogous were even higher, as anticipated. But in the circle? These were *lower*! The average in several circles was around 20 cpm, some were even lower than that. There was an eerie impression of 'holes in the landscape', anomalies neatly marked by the circles, since the anomaly appeared to occur just within the immediate vicinity of the circle. Did the circle mark an anomaly or did it *create* an anomaly by blocking background? Were the circles 'refuges' in the high radiation background? How could ancient man have known about radiation, how could the environment have furnished clues to enable the farmers to pick up signs of a *below* background level? How did the Rollright result fit in?

So many questions from a 'simple' control experiment! Since then this pattern of below background anomalies has been repeated in western Britain at many sites. In some cases the readings inside the circle were well below 20 cpm—below the level that, at Rollright, seemed to be coming from purely cosmic ray sources. How could this be so? Could these 'refuges' screen-off cosmic rays? We were moving into very strange and disturbing territory indeed.

BREAKTHROUGH

The strange results from Cornwall had underlined the fact that for the work on energy anomalies to proceed, a wholly different effort had to be made, with a comparable increase in funding and resources, both in terms of personnel and equipment. That we had established unusual energetic phenomena at stone circles was becoming increasingly beyond doubt, but we had now reached a crisis point, having exhausted our immediate funding

134

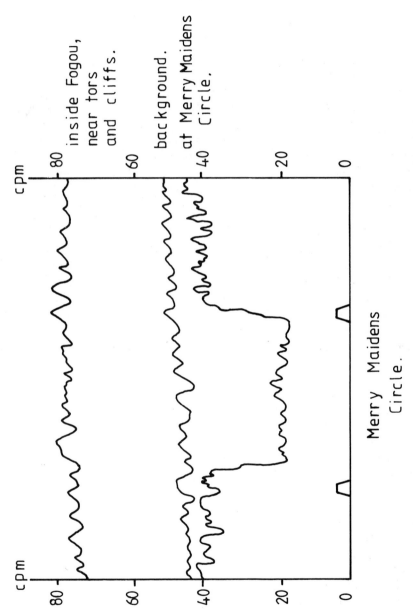

Fig 42. Simple Geiger Measurements in Cornwall. The higher background is related to the greater level of radioactivity from granite compared with limestone. The low readings inside the circle were totally unexpected.

135

and the initial programme. The Dragon Project had been struggling for over four years in the face of daunting odds and we now needed to present our results in a forum that would emphasise the seriousness of our effort and act as a springboard to raise additional funding at an appropriate level.

I had thought about the possibilities of publishing in the scientific literature but I had misgivings about the chances of such a paper being accepted. Although I was now on the faculty of the Institute of Archaeology, I could not honestly write from this address or use this connection. We were still out in the wilderness, despite having reached a point that I had aimed for long ago. We could now simply present what we had done, so that others coming after could follow it up; we had been scientific within the constraints of our resources and we had raised any discussion above the level of our individual veracity or gullibility. Of course, it was possible that we had made a glaring fundamental error somewhere, or we might have missed some stunningly obvious point that publication would quickly show up. How to go about this, at a level beyond that of the fringe magazines, who would quickly and uncritically accept anything with a scientific ring to it, was a problem with no obvious solution.

In the Spring of 1982, while I was deeply embroiled in my orthodox archaeology and engaged on a series of excavation visits in the USA and France, the chance for publication emerged. John Steele, in contact with *New Scientist*, arranged a meeting with the then Features Editor, Colin Tudge, who invited me, from my academic stance, to write a major feature article for the Autumn (for obvious reasons I insisted on avoiding August!). He was sympathetic about my desire to write a flat, prosaic account devoid of speculation, and in between long transatlantic flights and waiting in airport lounges, the article took shape.

I could not, of course, avoid speculating on the Geiger anomalies. The realities behind the anomalous lows, the significance in terms of ancient detection, the meaning of the highs at Rollright and later Moel-ty-Uchaf, all puzzled me, but I held that tightly in check. Let us simply show the phenomenon to be there, and then anyone can speculate as well as I can! But, whatever we thought, however bizarre the findings, they seemed to be real. The silence *was* broken, but what were the circles saying?

As the publication deadline for the *New Scientist* piece drew near, I went through several crises of conscience. I realised, with painful clarity, that whereas articles in fringe magazines and foreign radio went below the academic radar, there was no way that the *New Scientist* article could be ignored. Many people would read it; if it was nonsense it would be shot down in flames, if not it might launch the whole project into a new era. Whichever way the dice went, I had nailed my colours to the Project mast

136

41. An interesting test for the ultrasonic programme will be the monitoring of this circle at Moncrieff, Perthshire. Moved to its present location in the grounds of Moncrieffe House, because of a road-widening scheme at its original site, will it retain any activity or will that reside in the site, or will all activity be lost? And if activity is lost, shall we ever know why? (Photo: Duncan MacNeil)

and I was trading whatever reputation I had built on the acceptance of a genuine scientific effort in extremely unorthodox surroundings.

On 21st October, 1982, exactly four years after that first dawn at Rollright, the article appeared, only slightly edited and trimmed by *New Scientist*. I waited for the heavens to fall about my shoulders, feeling rather like Asterix's chieftain. I waited. And waited. A few desultory letters appeared in *New Scientist*'s columns, but apart from that, nothing.

The whole account seemed to have fallen into an academic black hole. Perhaps I had, unwittingly or unerringly, hit the target I had aimed for. Scientific critics were denied scoffing criticism by the implied and stated offer to check everything independently. The mystics had scientific verification from a totally unexpected source, so unexpected that they were

137

42. The 'Mind Mirror' meets the Kingsmen. Maxwell Cade looks on as John Steele experiences the stones and the 'Mind Mirror' picks up his brain patterns. This 'geopsychic' aspect of the Project will become increasingly important as the physical monitoring programme becomes more refined and reproducible and the physical activity of the sites becomes quantified. (Photo: Paul Devereux)

at a loss for words—for once! Here indeed were circles of silence, a pebble dropped in a still pond, with deep, solemn ripples moving ever and ever outwards. Was this *really* the secret of the circles: energy anomalies that defined their location, with the discovered geometry and astronomy merely adjuncts of this fundamental feature? Was this *it*?

The silence deepened. Unconsciously breathing a sigh of relief that the academic lightning had not struck me, I dived back into the world of orthodox archaeology, and I wondered just why there had been no reaction.

For six months the silence held. And then in March 1983 everything happened at once. I was approached by BBC TV *Nationwide* who wanted to film at Rollright, and this eventually triggered an interview for a lengthy article, subsequently extended, in the *Guardian*. That brought a considerable response from high and low. My interviewer, Susan Thomas, was inundated with mail, and most of it bore out my original contention—we had actually become *respectable*. Science fact had merged with science fiction and I could actually discuss this work with archaeologists in a sane and reasonable manner. The Dragon Project had done its job, it had found anomalies and created a new climate, although most of the work is still to be presented.

DRAGON RAMPANT

Matters did not, of course, end there. All the time the Project has continued, exploring the avenues opened up during the heady days of discovery and, whereas in this book I have described the view of the skyline, there are many other perspectives of the Project which will be elaborated at a later date, by those most closely involved.

The development of the anomaly picture and its substantiation by independent monitors with independent machinery, both at Rollright and at an increasing range of other sites, has encouraged the first forays into speculation about the significance of these anomalies.

Perhaps the most fruitful direction has been the consideration that these phenomena may have been connected with something tangible or visible that marked these sites as strange or mysterious, and that this was indeed seized upon by a priesthood and formed the basis of a veneration which was ultimately enshrined in stone.

What could have been perceived directly? One possibility is to consider the scope for energy transduction more generally than we have done so far in this book. Many energetic changes are accompanied by additional forms of energy, and sometimes this will involve the production of visible light. Such phenomena have been discussed in relation to 'earthquake lights' and even given the name of triboluminescence (light produced by friction) by analogy with piezoelectricity. At Rollright, for example, the nearby fault might well produce light and ultrasound under frictional stress; perhaps these phenomena were localised at the site in neolithic times and the erection of the circle enshrined this point which was then held in religious awe.

While there is a possible route here to relate the ultrasound to the site location, it says nothing for the Geiger anomalies: high local radioactive concentrations might produce corresponding local mutations which could have been observed and held in awe, but the developing pattern of subnormal anomalies does not support this argument very well. Perhaps, instead, one is looking at the marking of an anomaly which could be sensed rather than explained in terms of the Geiger readings? These findings seem to be the central mystery of the Project; no plausible mechanism for their existence or localisation can be readily put forward, whereas with the hotspots and ultrasonic emissions, at least a mechanism and a location hypothesis are possible.

Looking in this direction, an assumption has been made that the activity of the site is paramount and that the stones themselves simply mark an anomaly. Perhaps this is not so. Perhaps the structure or even geometry of the stones themselves augment or actually create the anomaly: the potential mechanism for ultrasound production is there in the inner structure of the

139

stone, and while one may look for concentrations of radioactive elements in the stones chosen for the site, the cause of positive anomalies may lie closer to hand. In the Geiger work, the sophisticated machines which could discriminate between the different components of the radiation showed convincingly that the major component was β-radiation.

This form of radiation consists of electrons expelled from the nucleus of a disintegrating atom and is detected on the basis of its negative charge. The Geiger counter will not necessarily distinguish between such a nuclear electron and one that is emitted by a surface, such as freshly exposed metal, for example. These 'exo-electrons' may therefore be detected with a Geiger counter which will respond in the same way to them as to nuclear electrons. In the various mechanisms of energy transduction and storage which ultimately depend upon the reservoir of trapped and mobile electrons in the stone lattice, discharges of such electrons might conceivably account for such high levels of Geiger readings, although the feeble penetrating power of such radiation poses problems of detection even feet away from the circle or active site.

So the puzzle continues and, as fresh data are gathered and developed, such speculation may be put increasingly to the test. Yet the major conundrum remains: are the anomalies emanating from the site, circle or both? One way to disentangle this problem is to find an anomaly site with no circle (or one which once contained a now vanished circle) and erect one and monitor before and after; another approach would be to erect a circle on a randomly selected inactive site and see if activity is induced by the construction and how this depends upon the geometry selected. Yet another possibility is to find a circle which has been physically moved from its location and restored intact elsewhere: this possibility actually exists at the stone circle of Moncrieff in Perthshire, Scotland.

Some years ago this circle was physically moved some hundreds of yards from its location to make way for a road-widening scheme. The circle was relocated in the grounds of Moncrieffe House. Would such a relocated circle be active? This would certainly make an interesting test of the Project findings, both at the new location and at the old one which is now buried beneath concrete and asphalt. But what if the new site is active? Would this mean that the initial geometry or the actual stone itself is important, or would activity have been conferred upon the new location? The problems of interpretation that such a test open up highlight the importance of measurement in this type of work—without it there is only endless speculation.

140

EPILOGUE

Few things in life have neat and tidy endings, least of all anything to do with the pursuit of that will o' the wisp, 'earth energy'. Can we say that there is such a thing, and does it relate at all to the location of the circles by ancient man?

Nothing as yet achieved by the Project proves this one way or the other. There seem to be anomalies at the circles which are not apparent at a very wide range of control sites. It may be a factor in the earth, it may be a consequence of the orientation of the stones, it may be a conjunction of the two factors. Either way, we are led to think that, somehow and at some level, the megalith builders had an awareness of the phenomenon. As a physical scientist, I try to avoid the controversy over extra-sensory perception, feeling that a demonstrable and repeatable ESP phenomenon will bring forth a rational explanation, irrespective of preconceptions. Yet the phenomena uncovered in the Project cannot be perceived by our unaided sensory system. If the anomalies are attributes of some more fundamental feature, then that, too, is likely to be beyond our limits of direct perception, unless we suggest that it is accessible to some form of heightened awareness.

Such a suggestion, while opening the floodgates on the association of the circles with witchcraft and shamanism, where heightened perception is commonly induced by hallucinogenic drugs, could still be consistent with any religion practised by the early farmers; access to hallucinogens through crop and food contaminants was only too likely in primitive farming methods and may even have been consciously sought after.

Although there is no answer at this stage, we can see that the range of possibilities does not necessarily conflict with the findings of orthodox archaeology; nor do we discredit either the geometric or astronomical lobbies by incorporating energy anomaly aspects into the overall picture. They can all coexist, even though the new recruit does make life a little uncomfortable for the established members!

141

Is there a deeper-rooted anomaly that could be perceived in any way? It is difficult to think of the immediate usefulness of ultrasound pulsing or of enhanced or diminished radioactivity. My original contention was to look for a fundamental property of stone, and in Chapter 3 we saw two potential sources of energy: a discharge of electrons and an energy transduction in the lattice. A static discharge via the stone is possible both as a phenomenon and as something directly perceivable. Could this lie at the root of the anomaly, and could the suggested siting of stone circles along geological fault lines form the basis for an energy anomaly located in the earth at these points?

We stand at the edge of an abyss where something is going on in the lower depths. *Something* gives a shadow of substance to the wild folktales and legends. Out of the silence come the ultrasonic pulsing and the click of the Geiger counter, but they are still faint and difficult to comprehend.

Let me end, therefore, on an upbeat note, with an anecdote to match the way the story started. At the critical stage of the Project, in the Autumn of 1980, when I had returned to teaching from my year on the archaeological heights, I was invited to examine a thesis on stone circles for an American university. It dealt with psychic impressions of the circles and the student, who was psychically 'gifted', had an interest in ancient music and wanted to experience directly the music we all think of as being played in the Stone Age ceremonies. The basis of the dissertation was that, despite a vivid 'psychic access' to the neolithic gatherings, the ceremonies appeared to be held in total silence.

How could one assess this? The observation that it was an unexpected result told in its favour, but there was something even more compelling. The student 'read' me in our discussions like an open book. I was told that I would be awarded the Research Fellowship I was applying for and that after two years, despite my application for five years, I would move on to become the Director of a Research Institute and that I would write this book. I could see no prospect of any of these things coming about, but they have happened, and as I finish this book I have been appointed to direct the Research Institute. Coincidence, perhaps, but it is a true anecdote and it throws a wholly different perspective onto the circles of silence, where we began our quest.

FURTHER READING

The books and articles listed below deal with various aspects of the work on stone circles mentioned in the text, and the interested reader may like to use them as an introduction to the wider fields of study touched upon. In no way do they constitute an exhaustive bibliography: much of the Dragon Project work remains to be published as primary literature.

The Dragon Project

DEVEREUX, Paul. *Earth Lights*, 1982, Turnstone Press.

DEVEREUX, Paul, MacCARTNEY, Paul, and ROBINS, Don. 'Bringing UFOs down to Earth', *New Scientist*, 1 September, 1983, pp 627–630.

ROBINS, Don. 'The Dragon Project and the Talking Stones', *New Scientist*, 21 October, 1982, pp 166–171.

Stone Circles and Prehistory

ATKINSON, R. J. C. *Stonehenge*, 1979, Penguin Books.

BURL, Aubrey. *The Stone Circles of the British Isles*, 1976, Yale University Press.

HAWKINS, Gerald S. *Stonehenge Decoded*, 1970, Fontana Books.

LANG, Lloyd and Jennifer. *The Origins of Britain*, 1980, Routledge & Kegan Paul.

MACKIE, E. *The Megalith Builders*, 1976, Phaidon Press.

MICHELL, John. *Megalithomania*, 1982, Thames & Hudson.

PIGGOTT, Stuart. *Ruins in a Landscape*, 1976, Edinburgh University Press.

THOM, A. *Megalithic Sites in Britain*, 1967, Oxford University Press.

The Secret World of Stone

ALI OMAR, M. *Elementary Solid State Physics*, 1975, Addison & Wesley.

ROBINS, G. V., SALES, K. D., and MacNEIL, D. A. C. 'Ancient Spins', *Chemistry in Britain*, October 1984, pp 894–899, Royal Society of Chemistry.

143

Folklore

ALEXANDER, Marc. *British Folklore, Myth and Legend*, 1982, Weidenfeld & Nicolson.
BORD, Janet and Colin. *The Secret Country*, 1976, Elek Books.

Science and Religion

BOHM, David. *Causality and Chance in Modern Physics*, 1984, Routledge & Kegan Paul.
CAPRA, Fritjof. *The New Tao of Physics*, 1984, Flamingo.
DAVIES, Paul. *God and the New Physics*, 1983, Dent.
HAWKINS, Gerald S. *Mindsteps to the Cosmos*, 1984, Souvenir Press.
HUXLEY, Francis. *The Way of the Sacred*, 1980, W. H. Allen.
MICHELL, John. *The View over Atlantis*, 1973, Abacus Books.

Divining

GRAVES, Tom. *Dowsing*, 1976, Turnstone Press.
HITCHINGS, Francis. *Pendulum*, 1977, Fontana.

Ancient Alignments

DEVEREUX, Paul, and THOMSON, Ian. *The Ley Hunter's Companion*, 1979, Thames & Hudson.
WATKINS, Alfred. *The Old Straight Track*, 1925, Methuen. Paperback edition, 1974, Abacus Books.